WE WILL SEND FOR SOME OF OUR LOVING NEIGHBORS AND BE MERRY ALTOGETHER, UNTIL CHILDERMAS-DAY BE PAST AND GONE. IN WHICH TIME MY WIFE JOAN SHALL LAY APPLES IN THE FIRE TO ROAST, MY MAN WILLIAM SHALL TELL THEE A MERRY TALE, AND MY MAID MARGARET SHALL SING THE MELODIOUS CARROLS OF SEVERAL PLEASANT TUNES; AND SO WE'L BE HIGLY PIGLY ONE WITH ANOTHER.

A BOOK OF
CHRISTMAS
CAROLS

HARPER AND ROW,

PUBLISHERS

NEW YORK, EVANSTON,

AND LONDON

A BOOK OF

CHRISTMAS

CAROLS

Selected and Illustrated by

HAIG AND REGINA

SHEKERJIAN

Arranged for Piano, with Guitar Chords, by

ROBERT DE CORMIER

U 9

Words and melody of "Carol of the Birds" and "Little Jesus Sweetly Sleep" from the *Oxford Book of Carols,* published by the Oxford University Press, reprinted by permission. The carol entitled "A Mince Pie or a Pudding" is an adaptation of words and music of the same title that appeared in *The Gift to Be Simple,* by Edward Deming Andrews, published by Dover Publications, Inc., and reprinted through permission of the publishers.

FIRST EDITION

LIBRARY OF CONGRESS CATALOG CARD NUMBER: 63-16543

Book designed by the Shekerjians

The carols in this book have been classified as to type, and the book divided into eight sections, each devoted to one specific type. These carols come from many countries and many periods of time. Unfortunately, due to limitations of space, many beautiful carols have had to be omitted.

Wherever an original version of a carol was available, it was followed precisely. In other English or American carols we have tried to select the most authoritative source.

The authors wish to thank the following who helped with translations:

Ludvik Durchanek	Czech and Polish carols
Selma Stigberg deCormier and Ulla Löfgren	Swedish carols
Pedro Garcia	Spanish and Puerto Rican carols

Autography   Maxwell Weaner   *Music Editor*   Bob Silverman

A chill wind blew off the Tiber. People drew themselves in, hunched their shoulders up around their necks, clutched their purchases closer to their shivering bodies. It was December, and the city of Rome bustled with preparations for the feast of Saturnalia. Everyone was out shopping—senators in spotless white togas, soldiers of the Praetorian guard, artisans, slaves, all the people of Rome, both rich and poor. The streets, narrow and always crowded, were choked now with people pushing and jostling, anxious to buy. Children whimpered, tugged at their mothers' robes. Periodically, messengers elbowed their way through the crowd. An occasional cart, careening under a heavy load, sent everyone scurrying to safety.

Stalls in the Subura were piled high with linen cloth, baubles of gold, wigs, wine, and all kinds of good-smelling holiday foods. Children covered their ears while grownups shouted above the noise, dickering with the stall keepers. The noise was deafening, but the noise in the Subura today was a happy noise, a glad, intoxicating noise. This was Saturnalia. During the too-brief, dreamlike days of this festival, the slaves of Rome were as free men. As equals now could they meet their masters, sit at table with them, throw dice with them, speak freely. This was the season not only of high festivity but of general good will. Quarrels were suspended or forgiven. No war was declared. Friends feasted together, presents were given to children and to friends, and hymns were sung in honor of Saturn as we sing carols of Christmas today.

While the slaves and the plebians shopped in the Subura, the prominent and the wealthy of Rome were picking and choosing from the treasures in the market near the Forum. A tortoise shell comb, a crystal goblet; silk from China, perfumes and brilliant embroideries from Alexandria; a goose, a succulent pig for the feast; figs, dates, rich wine. And the greens—holly, pine, bay leaves, laurel—all kinds of greens, pungent and sweet, to decorate the house for Saturnalia. "Buy! Buy here! To please our god, Saturn!"

Saturn, in addition to being the Protector of the Sowers and the Seed, was also the symbol of a legendary golden age of plenty when all men lived together in happiness as equals. He was honored each year in December, the time of the winter solstice.

Not only the Romans but all mankind was accustomed to celebrating this time of year with a holiday of great joy and high festivity—a celebration to the sun which would soon rise higher in the sky and bring the earth and man again to spring. Egyptian, Hebrew, Chinese, Mayan, Norseman, Greek, Roman—for all peoples this was the time of resting from the toils of herding and farming, the time for beaching the long ships and hanging away the shields and the axes. This was man's time for feasting, for gathering together in friendship; the time of peace, the time for mirth and jollity, for joy. And man, in his joy, has always danced and sung and told stories, and, in many cultures, decorated his temples and his houses with garlands of evergreen, the symbol of the triumph of life over death.

When the Christian Church came into existence, it naturally protested against these festivals but, since it was impossible to get the people to give up their ancient holiday of joy and freedom, the Church simply converted many parts of the pagan festival into the festival of Christ's birth. As such, Christmas first came into existence about 336 A.D. and gradually made its way east, west, and north from Rome.

ost historians agree that, although the exact date of Christ's birth is still wrapped in obscurity, He was born not in December but at some time closer to the Feast of Passover. The period of twelve days linking together Christmas (December 25) and Epiphany (January 6) was declared a festal tide by the Council of Tours in 567. As a single word, however, "Cristesmesse" does not appear until 1131. The phrase "Christmas carols" first appears in print in the sixteenth century in little books from the presses of Wynkyn de Worde and Richard Kele in England.

The birthplace of the true Christmas carol is Italy where, in the thirteenth century, St. Francis brought religion out from its "Latin" cloister and made of it a warm and human thing, a part of, rather than separated from, life. Here, in the thirteenth century, in the poems of another inspired Franciscan, Jacopone da Todi, comes the first real outburst of Christmas joy in a popular tongue. From Italy the carol then spread quickly to all those countries where Christianity existed. Although the word "carol" originally meant ring dance and did not necessarily apply to Christmas, during the fifteenth century it gradually came to mean "song" not necessarily accompanied by dancing. Before 1550, "carol" was defined by a definite form—a group of uniform stanzas with a burden which begins the song and is repeated after each stanza. Today the word "carol" is synonymous for most people with any song relating to Christmas.

Until one remembers that the Puritan distrusted and therefore heartily disliked and sternly disapproved of any celebration of Christmas, it is difficult to believe that it was not until the nineteenth century that Christmas became a popular holiday in America. In New England Christmas was outlawed until the second half of the last century. Until 1856, December 25 was a common workday in Boston, and as late as 1870 classes were held in the public schools there on Christmas Day. It was the coming of the Irish and the Germans toward the middle of the century, followed by the Swedes, the Italians, the Poles and other central Europeans that gave Christmas a chance to flower in this country. Today, of course, fed by the folk customs of many nations, it is the most widely celebrated of all holidays in America.

The general tendency of modern civilization, with its scientific spirit and its devastating commercialism, has been to destroy traditional customs. But, even for the most skeptical and enlightened of moderns, there is usually a Christmas for the children, who, totally unenlightened, still bob and hop in speechless joy around the room of Christmas. For many adults there is also the custom of "good cheer" —the eating and drinking together in friendship—which is joined to, and contributes to, a feeling of goodwill toward the world at large. For most people there is a brief giving way to sentiments and traditions ordinarily rejected, and a comprehension, temporary though it may be, not only of the Christian concept of the brotherhood of man but of the long roots we all have in a common heritage that began long before there was a Christmas to sing about. It has been said that "Emotionally we are hundreds of thousands of years old; rationally we are embryos."

At any rate, as the Tradesman says to Christmas, in *Make Room for Christmas* (1675):

"We will send for some of our loving Neighbors and be merry altogether, until Childermas-day be past and gone. In which time my wife Joan shall lay Apples in the fire to Roast, my Man William shall tell thee a merry tale, and my Maid Margaret shall sing the melodious Carrols of several pleasant Tunes; and so we'l be higly pigly one with another."

Contents

SHEPHERD CAROLS

Since antiquity, shepherds have piped on the hills the joy of life and its sorrows. Through hollow reeds, through horns of animals and bones of birds, their songs have echoed out across Egypt, Israel, China, and Peru; through all of Europe, through most of the world. Vergil tells of "the sweet numbers that the shepherds sang," and it is known that the most primitive form of the bagpipe is found among the shepherds of all lands.

The songs of the shepherds, their measured, graceful dances, although they exist today only in those communities which are still predominantly pastoral, exist everywhere in the Christian world's subconscious as an integral part of Christmas. Perhaps this is so because, of all the events recorded in the Gospel, the story of the angel appearing to the shepherds and the shepherds' response is the one event with which all men can identify. It is the truly human part of the story of Christ's birth.

Nowhere is this picture of the shepherd more vividly portrayed than in the medieval "mysteries," that vast cycle of plays telling the story of the Bible from the Creation to the Last Judgment. These plays were common not only in England but in all European countries also. Each country gave to these plays its own particular flavor, but all followed a fairly similar pattern. There are usually three shepherds, it is night, they are watching their flocks and talking together of their hard lot—the oppression of the rich, the diseases of their sheep, a shrewish wife, the cold weather. They are "al lappyd in sorow." They eat their supper then with great relish, seasoning it with appropriate and often bawdy comments; they lie down to sleep; and suddenly the angel appears singing *Gloria in excelsis*.

Although there are many local-color variations up to this point (many of lusty comic nature), they all end with the shepherds going to Bethlehem. There at the stable they give their gifts, "the only ones they have," to the Child.

Their offerings of homely gifts—a hat, a precious pipe, mittens to keep the Child's hands warm, a rattle "which goes 'clic, clac' at His ear," a spoon, a bob of cherries, a bird in a cage; their joyous invitations to dance, to "bring your pipes and bring your drum"; their anxious urgings to "hurry, hurry,"—these are the human, the simple and natural reactions to the "good news of great joy."

When the shepherd at the stable speaks to the Child, he speaks with charming sincerity, devoid of all artifice:

> "Nowe, childe, although thou be comon from God,
> And be God thy selfe in thy manhoode,
> Yet I knowe that in thy childehoode
> Thou wylte for sweete meate loke,
> To pull downe aples, peares, and plumes,
> Oulde Joseph shall not nede to hurte his thombes,
> Because thou hast not pleintie of crombes,
> I geve thee heare my nutthocke."
>
> (The Chester Plays)

And, as he speaks, so does the shepherd sing.

Shepherds come a-running

With gentle spirit

Traditional Polish

1. Shep-herds come a- run- ning in- to Beth - le - hem, Mer- ri - ly they sing and play their
2. Hap- pi - ly they of - fer Him their gifts so sweet, Rai-sins, grapes and cit- rons, ap- ples

pipes, hear ___ them! Deep - ly now they bow to Ma - ry, won-d'ring how to
red for a treat. Rob - in of - fers Him his spar - row, sing- ing soft- ly

greet the Child, Ti - ny Child: Deep - ly now they bow to
all the while, To the Child; Tom and Ni - co - de - mus

Ma - ry, won - d'ring how to greet the Child, Je - sus mild.
bring a new - born lamb, a tink - ling bell; Wish Him well.

3. Merrily the shepherds all are dancing round,
Shepherds singing, sheep bells ringing, pipes gayly sound!
Deeply now they bow to Mary, singing farewell to the Child,
Tiny Child:
Deeply now they bow to Mary, singing farewell to the Child,
Jesus mild.

Rise up, shepherd, and follow

An American Negro spiritual, one of many which a group of officers in the Union Army collected during the Civil War. Entitled *Slave Songs of the United States,* these were published in 1867.

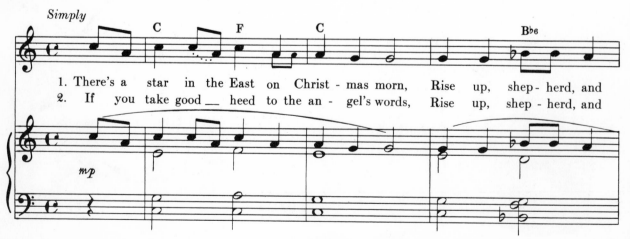

Simply

1. There's a star in the East on Christ - mas morn, Rise up, shep - herd, and
2. If you take good ___ heed to the an - gel's words, Rise up, shep - herd, and

fol - low! ___ It will lead to the place where the Sa - viour's born, _____
fol - low! ___ You'll for - get yo' ___ flocks, you'll for - get your herds, _____

Rise up, shep - herd, and fol - low! ___
Rise up, shep - herd, and fol - low! ___ Leave your sheep and

Chorus:

leave your lambs; Rise up, shep - herd, and fol - low! ___

Leave your ewes and leave your rams; ___ Rise up, shep-herd, and
fol-low! ___ Fol - - low! Fol - - low!
Rise up, shep-herd, and fol-low! ___ Fol - low the star of
Beth - le - hem, ___ Rise up, shep-herd, and fol - low! ___

16

❋ Pastores a Belén ❋
SHEPHERDS TO BETHLEHEM

Traditional Puerto Rican

1. To Beth - le - hem let's go, _____ O shep - herds, do _ not tar - ry; With
Pas - to - res, a Be lén _____ Va - mos con a - le - grí - a; Que

hap - py hearts let's go _____ To greet the Son _ of Ma - ry. A-
ha na - ci - do ya _____ El Hi - jo de _ Ma - ri - - a. A-

llí, _____ A - llí, Je - su a - waits us there. _____ A-
llí, _____ a - llí, Nos es - pe - ra Je - sús. _____ A-

there. _____ Sweet cakes we bring and hon - ey too, To give to Him, the
sús. _____ Lle - ve - mos pues tur - ro - nes y miel Pa - ra o fre - cer al

lit - tle Je - su. Sweet cakes we bring and hon - ey too, To give to Him, the
Ni - ño Man-uel, Lle - ve - mos pues tur-ro-nes y miel Pa-ra of-re-cer al

lit - tle Je - su. Come then, shep-herds, Come — with me, Come — and see the
Ni - ño Man-uel. Va - mos, va - mos, va - mos a ver, Va - mos a ver al

sweet ba - by Je - su, Come — and see the new — born King.
re - cien na - ci - do, Va - mos a ver Al Ni - ño Man-uel.

Lippai

Paraphrase of traditional German words

Tyrolean tune

Brightly

1. Lip - pai, __ a - wake, don't sleep! "What is that you
1. *Lip - pai, __ steh __ auf vom Schlaf!* "*Was ist denn __*

said?" I don't know how you can stay a - sleep! "This _____ is my
da?" *Mich wun - dert's __ dass __ d'schla - fen kannst.* "*Ich _____ schla - fe*

bed!" Come with me to the __ field. See there the won-der re-vealed!
schön." Geh mit mir auf die __ Weid, Schau was für Wun-der __ geit.

Look! It's __ as __ light as day! "What's ____ that you say?"
'S ist so __ licht __ wie am Tag. "Was _____ wär __ das?"

2. Sweet sound of singing fills the air!
　　"I can't hear a thing!"
　Come, take your pipe—let's go there!
　　"I am coming!"
　Angels sing joyfully,
　"He is born!" truthfully,
　Born a child as king today!
　　"Is that what they say?"

3. Bethlehem is the town.
　　"Who told you?"
　The angel spoke it all around!
　　"Is this really true?"
　A young maid both sweet and mild,
　Is mother of the child.
　Let's go where the star shines bright!
　　"Yes, you are right!"

4. A new king is born today!
　　"A child is king!"
　In stable rude he lies in hay!
　　"Oh, what a thing!"
　I'll ask his mother sweet,
　His name when soon we meet.
　Come, good friend, come with me!
　　"Yes, I want to see!"

4. *So schön ist keins geborn.*
　　"Wie das Kind!"
　Dass's auf dem Heu muss lieg'n.
　　"Is rechte Sünd!"
　Ich tu die Mutter fragn
　Ob ich's mit mir darf tragn;
　Ich hätt die grösste Freud.
　　"Du redst gescheit."

2. *Die Musik währt schon lang.*
　　"Ich hör nicht."
　Trag deine Pfeif auch bei dir!
　　"Bin schon gericht't."
　D'Engel, die singen ob'n:
　Es ist ein Kind geborn.
　Wenn's der Messias wär!
　　"Das wär rar."

3. *Bethlehem heisst der Ort!*
　　"Wer hat's gesagt?"
　Ich hab's vom Engel g'hört.
　　"Hast ihn gefragt?"
　Ein Jungfrau keusch und rein
　Soll seine Mutter sein,
　Dort wo der Stern brinnt.
　　"Geh nur geschwind!"

shepherds are singing

A dialogue carol

Dutch, fifteenth century

1. (1st shepherd): Shep-herds, I hear you cal - ling! I'm com - ing right a - way!_ (Other shepherds): Nö - el is what we're
2. (1st shepherd): Ap- ples and plums and cher - ries, New milk and but - ter sweet._ (2nd shepherd): Nut - meg and gol - den

cal - ling! Come, hur - ry! Don't de - lay! ___ *(Chorus)* Shep - herds are sing - ing and
hon - ey, A lit - tle cake of wheat. ___

danc - ing so mer - ri - ly, Shep-herds are play-ing glad songs on their pipes to - day. ___

3. *(3rd shepherd):*

> Raisins and figs and pears ripe,
> A basket of new bread.

(4th shepherd):

> Here! You can have my new pipe,
> And take my cloak bright red! *(Chorus)*

4. *(All shepherds):*

> Lullaby now, sweet Jesus.
> Bye bye, dear baby, sleep;
> Sleep close to your mother,
> We must go watch our sheep! *(Chorus)*

This melody is *Herders hij is gebooren,* a Dutch carol of the fifteenth century, for which new words have been written.

NOEL

Haut, haut, Peyrot

A "noël ancien" from *Chansons et Airs Populaires* edited by M. Frederic Rivares, 1868.

1. Wake up, Pierre, a - wa - ken, Come hear the mu - sic gay! How
2. O come, Pierre, I __ beg you, Let's go and join them there! They

can you sleep this morn - ing, When dawn brings such a day? Can't you
go to lit - tle Je - su; He lies in sta - ble bare. Let us

hear the shep-herds sing-ing? Can't you see the star so bright? Joy-ful
run and hur-ry af-ter All our friends who go there too! Lit-tle

sounds the mu-sic ring-ing, With the dawn comes ro-sy light. Come and
Je-su, dar-ling ba-by, We will sing a song to you! Ma-ry,

join the hap-py sing-ing, Come see the pret-ty sight!
moth-er of the ba-by, How bles-sed is she too!

3. Oh, sing with joy and gladness,
   Play sweetly on your pipe!
   Antoine brings golden raisins,
   Arnaud brings cherries ripe;
   William brought his woolen mittens
   For the baby dear and small;
   Nicodemus has some honey,
   Marc has brought his bouncing ball!
   For sweet Mary and her baby,
   Noël sing we all!

While Shepherds Watched

Traditional English
(Hampshire air)

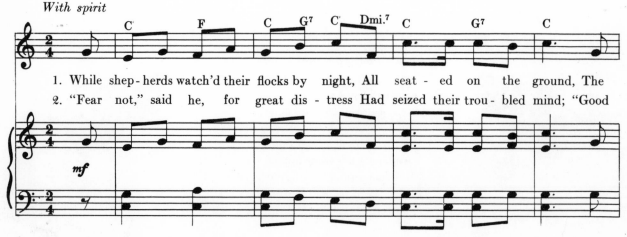

With spirit

1. While shep - herds watch'd their flocks by night, All seat - ed on the ground, The
2. "Fear not," said he, for great dis - tress Had seized their trou - bled mind; "Good

an - gel of the Lord came down And glo - ry shone a - round; And
ti - dings of great joy I bring To you and all man - kind; To

Dmi.⁷ G⁷ C G
glo - ry shone a - round,_____ And glo - ry shone a -
you and all man - kind,_____ To you and all man -

f

C G C
round, And glo - ry shone a - round; The an - gel of the Lord came down And
kind, To you and all man - kind; Good ti - dings of great joy I bring To

p

poco a poco cresc.

Dmi.⁷ G⁷ C D.C.
glo - ry shone a - round, And glo - ry shone a - round._____
you and all man - kind, To you and all man - kind."_____

D.C.

f

Dance Carols

It is, apparently, as natural for man to dance as it is for him to speak, for as early as the Stone Age, dances became works of art. And, just as man's first house (after the cave or windbreak) was a circular hut, so too did his first dance take the form of a circle.

The circle seems instinctive to man, and the circle dance is found in all cultures. In fact it is seen today in the folk dances of modern Sweden and Austria, and in the ring games of children everywhere.

Dance has always been inextricably linked with the everyday life of primitive peoples, and it played an important role in all ancient civilizations, particularly in religious worship. As the Persian, Rumi, cried, "Whosoever knoweth the power of the dance, dwelleth in God." And, in Psalm 150, we are clearly told to "Praise him with the timbrel and dance."

For many long thousands of years, man could not conceive of life without dance. As late as the thirteenth and fourteenth centuries there was always dancing in a circle about the crèche in the churches of Europe on Christmas Eve. Until very recently, choir boys, dressed in antique black costumes and accompanied by string and wind instruments and by the clicking of castanets, sang and danced before the altar and around the praesepio in the cathedral of Seville. Today dancing still plays an important role in the Christmas Eve celebration of the Pueblo Indians in New Mexico. Here, two dance traditions have merged—that of the ancient tribe and that of early Spain.

Although today the word "carol" simply means a song that is sung at Christmas, it originally meant a round, or ring dance. The word itself (which first appears in extant English literature about 1300) probably derives from the Greek *choros*, meaning a dance, and perhaps also from *choraules*, meaning one who accompanies the dance.

Dancing was always looked upon with suspicion by the Church, although it was originally permitted along with other so-called pagan practices in early attempts to Christianize the people. With gradual social and economic changes created by a growing urbanization, however, the Church seized this opportunity to ban dancing within the sanctuary itself. But, even without Church opposition, urbanization would have destroyed this kind of dancing which is essentially a communal act. It cannot exist as such in any society where the individual rather than the community is predominant.

What is left of the dance carol today is seen at its best in Sweden where they still dance in a ring around the tree, singing with great gusto and an enviable, rollicking joy *"Nu är det Jul igen,"* *"Ritsch, ratsch, filibom!"* and a host of other equally wonderful songs.

In other countries, dance carols are merely sung, in spite of the fact that many are almost irresistible invitations to dance.

Fum, fum, fum!

After midnight Mass, called *Misa de Gallo* ("Mass of the Cock"), people promenade on the streets with torches, tambourines and guitars, singing and dancing and greeting one another. This carol is Catalan in origin, but has been adopted by all Spain. The "fum, fum, fum" (pronounced "foom" rather shortly) represents the strummed guitar.

Spanish

With marked rhythm

1. On De-cem-ber twen-ty- five, ___ Fum, fum, fum!
1. *Vein - te - cin - co   de   di - ciem-bre, Fum, fum, fum!*

On   De- cem- ber   twen-ty- five, ___ Fum,   fum,   fum!   Born is
Vein -te - cin - co   de   di - ciem - bre,   Fum,   fum,   fum!   Na - ci -

He   for   love   of   us,   The   Son   of   God, the Son of God;   Born is
do ha por   nues-tro a - mor,   El   Ni - ño   Dios; el Ni - ño Dios;   Hoy de

30

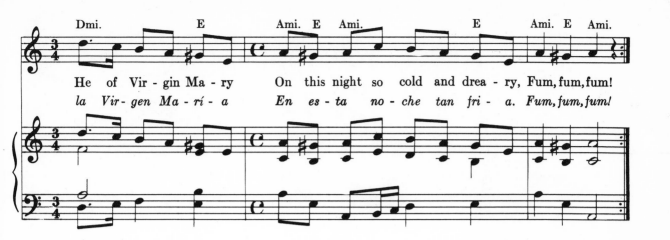

He of Vir - gin Ma - ry / On this night so cold and drea - ry, Fum, fum, fum!
la Vir - gen Ma - rí - a / En es - ta no - che tan fri - a. Fum, fum, fum!

2. Little birds out in the wood,
   Fum, fum, fum!
   Little birds out in the wood,
   Fum, fum, fum!
   Leave your berries bright and good,
   Please do come, O please do come!
   Make a soft and downy nest
   So the newborn Babe may rest,
   Fum, fum, fum!

3. Little stars up in the sky,
   Fum, fum, fum!
   Little stars up in the sky,
   Fum, fum, fum!
   See the little Jesus crying,
   Don't you cry, don't you cry;
   Fill the night with twinkling light,
   Oh little stars that shine so bright,
   Fum, fum, fum!

2. *Pajaritos de los bosques,*
   Fum, fum, fum!
   Pajaritos de los bosques,
   Fum, fum, fum!
   Vuestros hijos de coral,
   Abandonad, abandonad,
   Y formad un muelle nido
   A Jesús recien nacido,
   Fum, fum, fum!

3. *Estrellitas de los cielos,*
   Fum, fum, fum!
   Estrellitas de los cielos,
   Fum, fum, fum!
   Que a Jesús mirais llorar,
   Y no lloráis, y no lloráis,
   Alumbrad la noche oscura
   Con vuestra luz clara y pura,
   Fum, fum, fum!

Ritsch, ratsch, filibom!

Swedish

Gayly—with spirit

Ritsch, ratsch, fi - li - bom bom bom, fi - li - bom bom bom, fi - li -

bom bom bom! Ritsch, ratsch, fi - li - bom bom bom, fi - li - bom bom bom, fi - li - bom!

FINE

Wife Sö - der-strom, wife Sö - der-strom, wife Sö - der-strom, Wife Sö - der-strom and
lit - tle daugh - ter Rose:

1. They washed them-selves in o - cean wa - ter, o - cean wa - ter,
2. They gave us a lit - tle so - da wa - ter, so - da wa - ter,

o - cean wa - ter; Washed them-selves in o - cean wa - ter, o - cean wa - ter clear!
so - da wa - ter; Gave us a lit - tle so - da wa - ter, so - da wa - ter, punch!

Ritsch, ratsch, filibom bom bom,
filibom bom bom, filibom bom bom!
Ritsch, ratsch, filibom bom bom,
filibom bom bom, filibom!
Fru Söderström, fru Söderström, fru Söderström,
Fru Söderström och lilla mamsell Ros:

1. De tvättade sej i sjöavatten, sjöavatten, sjöavatten,
tvättade sej sjöavatten, sjöavatten klart.

2. De ge oss lite sodavatten, sodavatten, sodavatten,
ge oss lite sodavatten, sodavatten, punsch!

In Dulci Jubilo

This famous old German macaronic carol, found in a MS at Leipzig University, was supposedly written by the fourteenth century Dominican mystic, Heinrich Suso. Legend has it that one day a band of angels came to Suso to comfort him in his sufferings. They took him by the hand and danced with him while one of them sang a beautiful and happy song—*In dulci jubilo.* When both the song and the dance had ended, and all the angels had left, Suso sat down and wrote the words and music so that he might never forget how beautiful it was.

Robert L. dePearsall, 1795-1856

Fourteenth century German

1. *In dul - ci ju - bi - lo* _____ Let us our
2. *O Je - su par - vu - le!* _____ My heart is

hom - age show; _____ Our heart's joy re - cli -
sore for Thee! _____ Hear me I be - seech

neth *In prae - se - pi - o,* _____ And
thee! *O pu - er op - ti - me!* _____ My

Latin translations: (v. 1) *In dulci jubilo* (in sweet jubilation); *In praesepio* (in a manger); *Matris in gremio* (in His mother's lap); *Alpha es et O* (Thou art the beginning and the end); (v. 2) *O Jesu parvule* (O tiny Jesus); *O puer optime* (O best of Boys); *O Princeps gloriae* (O Prince of glory); *Trahe me post te* (Draw me after Thee); (v. 3) *Ubi sunt gaudia* (where are the joys?); *Nova cantica* (new songs); *In regis curia* (in the court of the King).

3. *Ubi sunt gaudia*
   If that they be not there?
   Angels there are singing
   Nova cantica,
   Sweet bells the while a-ringing
   In regis curia:
   O that we were there!
   O that we were there!

Oh, Who Would Be a Shepherd Boy

Traditional English

Moderately

1. Oh, who __ would be a shep - herd boy, And mind __ a flock of
3. Now then __ there came a shin - ing one, An an - gel of the

sheep, _____ While oth - er men and boys __ en - joy A
Lord; _____ With news __ of God's e - ter - nal Son, By

5. Then many more were heard to raise
   A cheerful hymn of mirth:
   "To God in heaven be endless praise;
   And peace to men on earth."

6. The shepherds' hearts were comforted
   By what was told to them.
   "And after what we've heard," they said,
   "Let's go to Bethlehem."

Ding Dong

This tune, as it appears in *Orchésographie* (a French book of dances published in 1588), is a Branle—a round dance accompanied by singing. Originally a village dance, in the seventeenth century it suddenly became popular with the aristocracy.

Tune: *Branle de l'Officiel*

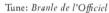

1. Ding dong! mer-ri-ly on high   The bells are gai-ly
2. Ding dong! Car-ol all the bells.   A-wake now, do not

ring-   ing;   Ding dong! hap-pi-ly re-ply   The an-gels all a-sing-ing.
tar-   ry!   Sing out, sound the good now-ells,   Je-su is born of Ma-ry.

Glo - ri - a Ho - san - na in ex - cel - sis.

3. Ring out, merry merry bells,
The angels all are singing.
Ding dong! Swing the steeple bells,
Sound joyous news we're bringing!

4. Hark now! Happily we sing,
The angels wish us merry!
Ding dong! Dancing as we bring
Good news from Virgin Mary.

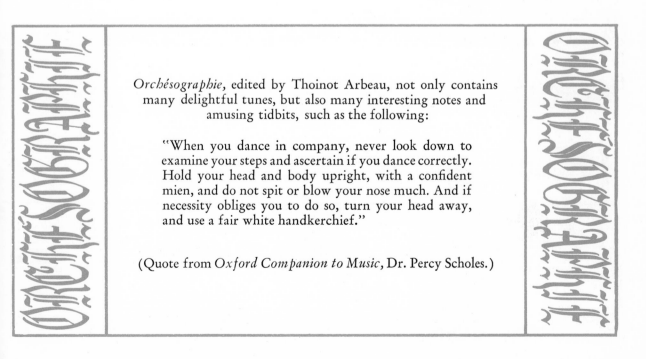

Orchésographie, edited by Thoinot Arbeau, not only contains many delightful tunes, but also many interesting notes and amusing tidbits, such as the following:

"When you dance in company, never look down to examine your steps and ascertain if you dance correctly. Hold your head and body upright, with a confident mien, and do not spit or blow your nose much. And if necessity obliges you to do so, turn your head away, and use a fair white handkerchief."

(Quote from *Oxford Companion to Music*, Dr. Percy Scholes.)

Christmas Day is Come

"Christmas comes but wanst a year/And when it comes it brings good cheer/And when it goes it laves us here/And what'll we do for the rest o' the year." .... Irish carolers' greeting rhyme

Paraphrase based on seventeenth century words

Traditional Irish melody

With spirit

1. Christ-mas Day is come; let's all pre-pare for mirth, With songs of joy and glad-ness, for Christ is come to earth. Here with-in the sta-ble, the new-born Ba-by lies, For Him sing all the an-gels; their sing-ing fills the skies. They

2. Ho-ly Maid and Ba-by, in sta-ble cold and bare; But where is there a pal-ace that could with this com-pare? Ma-ry is the Queen, in heav-en and on earth; Her Son is King of Kings; to Him she did give birth. He

40

hail with ad - o - ra - tion,"All Ho- ly," do they cry; They sing "Ho- san - na, Ho- ly, Ho -
comes to live a - mong us, to bring us peace and love; To show us we are broth-ers, both

ly In - fant," on high. They hail with ad - o - ra - tion, "All Ho- ly," do they cry; They
here ___ and a - bove. He comes to live a - mong us, to bring us peace and love; To

sing "Ho- san - na, Ho - ly, Ho - ly In - fant," on high.
show us we are broth- ers, both here ___ and a - bove.

3. "Holy, Holy, Holy," the joyous angels cry;
   And "Holy, Holy, Holy," we now do all reply.
   Three noble kings are coming with precious gifts so rare,
   But it is love we bring to Him in stable bare.
   And singing with the angels, Nowell, Nowell, Nowell,
   We worship little Jesus, Lord Immanuel.
   And singing with the angels, Nowell, Nowell, Nowell,
   We worship little Jesus, Lord Immanuel.

LULLABY
CAROLS

Since the lullaby is one of the oldest forms of expression in song, it is probably reasonable to assume that the lullaby was also one of the earliest Christmas songs.

Most cradle songs have, quite naturally, a rocking, lilting rhythm and a simple pure melody. There are beautiful ones from every country of the world where Christmas is celebrated, some dating back to the fourteenth and fifteenth centuries.

Some in this group are specifically called "cradle rocking" carols, the term coming from the German word *Kindelwiegen* which means "rocking of the child."

The custom of *Kindelwiegen* originated in Germany and Austria in the fourteenth century. In the beginning, cradle rocking was done by the priests, one impersonating the Virgin, the other, Joseph, with the choir and the people sharing in some of the singing. This is well demonstrated in the song, "Joseph, Dearest Joseph, Mine." Dancing at this time was common around the cradle, which eventually the people were allowed to rock with their own hands.

Cradle rocking was one of the things which enabled the Church to make Christianity a genuinely popular religion in Germany. As Dr. Alexander Tille said, "The Christ Child was the 'universal little brother of all children of earth,' and they (the Germans) acted accordingly, they lulled Him to sleep, they fondled and rocked Him, they danced before Him and leapt around Him *in dulci jubilo*."

In the sixteenth century, due to Church opposition and the growth of pseudo-classical taste, the custom of *Kindelwiegen* gradually disappeared from the churches although it survived for a long time in many convents and private homes.

Lullabies from all countries are, almost without exception, beautiful and, in one respect, identical: the mother lulling her child to sleep (even when that mother is Mary and the child, Jesus) is the same mother no matter where you find her in the world.

> *"So bless'd a sight it was to see*
> *How Mary rokked her son so fre!*
> *So frayre she rokked and songe 'by, by';*
> *Myn own dere moder, syng lulley!"*

What Child is This?

William Chatterton Dix, 1837-1898

English, sixteenth century

1. What Child is this, who, laid to rest, On Mary's lap is sleep - ing? Whom an - gels greet with an - thems sweet, While

2. Why lies He in such mean es - tate, Where ox and ass are feed - ing? Good Chris - tian, fear: for sin - ners here The

3. So bring Him incense, gold, and myrrh,
Come, peasant, king to own Him;
The King of kings salvation brings,
Let loving hearts enthrone Him. *(Refrain)*

The secular "Greensleeves," which was a very popular dance tune during the time of Queen Elizabeth, provides the melody for England's favorite cradle song.

Joseph, dearest Joseph mine

A fourteenth century German cradle-rocking carol.

Easily

1. Jo- seph, dear - est Jo - seph mine, Help me cra-dle the
2. Glad- ly, dear one, la - dy mine, I'll help cra-dle this

Child di- vine, God re-ward ___ thee and all thine In
Child of thine; God's own light on us both shall shine In

Par - a- dise, so prays the moth- er Ma - ry.
Par - a- dise, so prays the moth- er Ma - ry.

46

Joseph, lieber Joseph mein

Je - su, Je - su, Je - su, ____ He came to us at Christ - mas-tide, At Christ - mas - tide, at Christ - mas-tide In Beth - le - hem. ____ Men shall come from

far and wide To Beth - le - hem, _____ so prays the

moth - er Ma - - - - ry. _____

3. Peace to all that have goodwill!
   God, who heaven and earth doth fill,
   Comes to turn us away from ill,
   And lies so still
       Within the crib of Mary.

4. All shall come and bow the knee;
   Wise and happy their souls shall be,
   Loving such a divinity,
   As all may see
       In Jesus, Son of Mary.

5. Now is born Emmanuel,
   Prophesied once by Ezekiel,
   Promised Mary by Gabriel—
   Ah, who can tell
       Thy praises, Son of Mary.

6. Thou my lazy heart hast stirred,
   Thou, the Father's eternal Word,
   Greater than aught that ear hath heard,
   Thou tiny bird
       Of love, thou Son of Mary.

7. Sweet and lovely little one,
   Thou princely, beautiful, God's own Son,
   Without thee all of us were undone;
   Our love is won
       By thine, O Son of Mary.

8. Little man, and God indeed,
   Little and poor, thou art all we need;
   We will follow where thou dost lead,
   And we will heed
       Our brother, brother of Mary.

This carol could easily become a little Christmas play for children, with Joseph and Mary singing verses 1 and 2 before the chorus sings. The remaining verses provide six other solos, during the singing of which Mary and Joseph rock the cradle. With the singing of the last chorus, the children all dance around the cradle as the people did in medieval Germany.

Away in a Manger

According to Richard Hill, these words first appeared in print in
A Little Children's Book: for Schools and Families, published in 1885
by the Evangelical Lutheran Church in North America.

From *Notes*, published by the Library of Congress.

American, anonymous

1. A - way in a man - ger, No crib for His bed, The lit - tle Lord
2. The cat - tle are low - ing, The poor Ba - by wakes, But lit - tle Lord

Je - sus Laid down His sweet head; The stars in the heav - ens Look'd
Je - sus No cry - ing He makes. I love Thee, Lord Je - sus, Look

down where He lay; The lit - tle Lord Je - sus A - sleep in the hay.
down from the sky, And stay by my cra - dle Till morn - ing is nigh.

COVENTRY CAROL

Robert Croo, 1534-1591

Gently

Chorus: Lul - ly, lul - la, you lit - tle ti - ny child;
1. O sis - ters too, how may ___ we ___ do

By by lul - ly, lul - lay, You lit - tle ti - ny child, lul -
For to pre - serve this day, This poor ___ Young - ling for

ly, ___ lul - la, By, by, lul - ly lul - lay.
Whom we do sing, By, by, lul - ly lul - lay.

D. C.

When the religious drama left the sanctuary, Latin gave way to common speech and the plays, presented by the various guilds, were performed at designated "stations" about the town. Each guild was responsible for one episode (a "play") from the Bible, each doing the one most suggestive of its craft. The Shipwrights would do the building of the ark; the Goldsmiths, the story of the Magi; the Shearmen and Tailors, the slaying of the Innocents by Herod; and so on. The stage for these plays was a two-story wagon called a "pageant wagon"—the lower floor serving as a curtained dressing room. Drawn by either men or horses, the pageant wagons wound their way through the old crooked streets to find a new audience eagerly awaiting them at each station, which might be a square or some well-known spot such as the street in front of the abbey gate. The plays which re-enacted the Christmas scenes were called "Mysteries." Carols were an integral part of these medieval dramas but, unfortunately, most of the carol music has been lost.

The "Coventry Carol," one of the most beautiful of all lullaby carols, comes from the pageant of the Shearmen and Tailors Company at Coventry. It is recorded that Queen Margaret witnessed this play in 1456, although the earliest written form of the tune is dated 1591. This song is sung by the women of Bethlehem just before Herod's soldiers come in to slaughter their children.

2. Herod the king in his raging
Chargèd he hath this day,
His men of might in his own sight,
All young childrèn to slay. (*Chorus*)

3. That woe is me, poor child, for thee!
And ever morn and day,
For thy parting neither say nor sing
By, by, lully, lullay. (*Chorus*)

rocking song

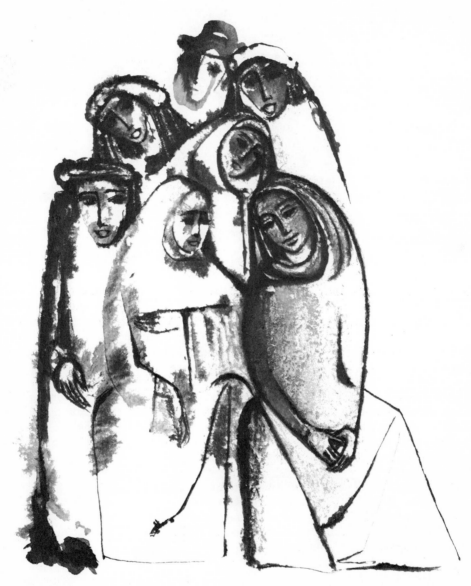

hajej, nynjej

Czech

Tenderly

1. Lit - tle Je - sus,
2. Ma - ry's lit - tle

sweet- ly __ sleep, do not __ stir; We will __ lend you a coat of __ fur.
Ba - by, __ sleep, sweet - ly __ sleep, Sleep in __ com - fort, __ slum-ber __ deep;

We will rock you, rock you, rock you, We will rock you, rock you, rock you:
We will rock you, rock you, rock you, We will rock you, rock you, rock you:

See the fur to keep you __ warm, Snug - ly __ round your __ ti - ny __ form.
We will serve you all we __ can, Dar - ling, __ dar - ling __ lit - tle __ man.

53

Lulajže Jezuniu

Sleep, little Jesus

Christmas in Poland is a family affair. On Christmas Eve, as soon as the first star appears in the sky, a festive supper is served. After supper the tree is lighted, carols are sung, and presents are opened. At midnight everyone goes to Mass, which is called *Pasterka*, the Shepherds' Mass.

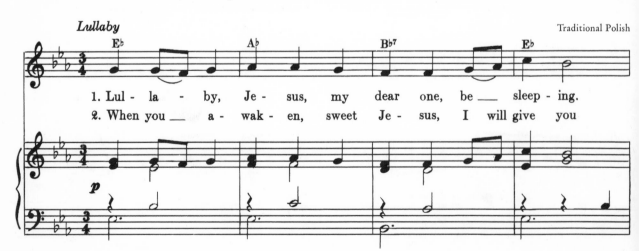

Lullaby

Traditional Polish

1. Lul - la - by, Je - sus, my dear one, be __ sleep - ing.
2. When you __ a - wak - en, sweet Je - sus, I will give you

3. Hush, He is sleeping while star shines above us;
   Like the bright sun is my sweet baby, Jesus. *(Refrain)*

1. *Lulajże Jezuniu, moja peretko,*
   Lulaj ulubione me pieścidetko.

(Refrain)
   Lulajże Jezuniu, lulajże, lulaj,
   A ty go matulu w ptaczu utulaj.

2. *Dam ja Ci słodkiego, Jesu, cukierku,*
   Rodzenków, migdałów co mam wpudetku. (Refrain)

3. *Lulajże przyjema oczom Gwiazdeczko,*
   Lulaj najsliczniejsze świata słoneczko. (Refrain)

EL·RORRO ROCKING·THE·CHILD

Traditional Mexican

Gently

A la ru - ru, chi-qui-to ni - ño, Duer-ma-se ya mi Je - su -
ru - ru, chi-qui-to ni - ño, Duer-ma-se ya mi Je - su -

sí - to. _____ 1. All the an - i - mals are stand-ing near, Ten-der-ly _____
sí - to. _____ 1. Ca-da an - i - mal y pá-ja - ro Tier-na-men-te

On each of the nine evenings before Christmas, the Mexican people re-enact the journey of Mary and Joseph from Nazareth to Bethlehem. This Christmas drama is called a *posada* or "inn." Each night a different house is selected to represent the inn, and each night when Mary and Joseph and the holy pilgrims arrive with lighted candles and sing, asking for shelter, they are at first refused. When Joseph finally says who he is and points out Mary, the innkeeper flings open the door and says, "Welcome! Welcome! Come into my humble home and be welcome!"

The procession then enters with joyous songs and, when the religious part of the *posada* has come to an end, everyone goes outside for a brilliant display of fireworks, dancing and eating, and for the *piñata*. The *piñata*, a clay jar covered with brightly colored crepe paper which has been twisted and shaped and fringed and curled, might be a magnificent bird or fish or star, or perhaps a baby burro. Each child in turn is now blindfolded and provided with a long stick, with which he flails the air above his head in valiant attempts to break the *piñata* hanging suspended in the center of the garden. Eventually some lucky child does break it, the candies, nuts and fruits spill out, and everyone scrambles happily about trying to get as many of the goodies as possible.

The last of the *posadas*, on Christmas Eve, is the most impressive of all. That night, upon entering the "inn," the Holy Infant is put into the manger and sung to sleep with "El Rorro."

2. Holy night, oh night of wondrous joy,
   Mary bore a son for us, a blessèd boy.
   A la ru-ru-ru, ah baby, dear one,
   Oh little Jesu, sleep, my son. *(Refrain)*

3. Angels all are singing merrily,
   Good news bringing, angels singing
       "Born is He."
   A la ru-ru-ru, ah baby, dear one,
   Oh little Jesu, sleep, my son. *(Refrain)*

2. *Noche venturosa, noche de alegría,*
   Bendita la dulce, divina María.
   A la ru-ru-ru, chiquito querido,
   Duermase ya mi Jesusito. (Refrain)

3. *Coros celestiales, con su dulce acento,*
   Canten la ventura de este nacimiento.
   A la ru-ru-ru, chiquito querido,
   Duermase ya mi Jesusito. (Refrain)

57

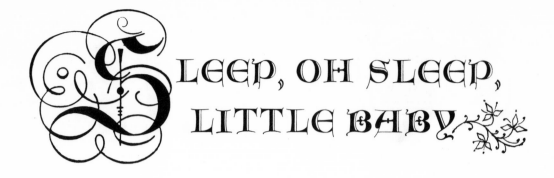

Sleep, Oh Sleep, Little Baby

Traditional Italian carol from *Storia Comparata Degli Usi Natalizi*, edited by Signor de Gubernatis; Milan, 1878.

Not too slowly

1. Sleep, my dar - ling ba - by, sleep. You are ___ king, This I ___ sing. Sleep, oh sleep, my dar - ling child, Watch I will keep,

2. Oh, my dar - ling ba - by dear, Why do you weep? Can't you ___ sleep? Close your eyes now, hush - a - by, Ho - ly are you,

DORMI, DORMI, O BEL BAMBIN

Paraphrase based on a translation by Countess Martinengo-Cesaresco in *Essays in the Study of Folk-Songs*, London, 1886.

Please don't weep. Close your eyes, my dar-ling, and sleep. _____
It is true. Sleep, oh sleep, my dar-ling ba-by. _____

Refrain:
Slum-ber soft-ly, in-fant so love-ly,
Sleep now gent-ly, dear ba-by mine. mine.

Carols of the Magi

According to legend, Melchior, Caspar, and Balthazar reached the Christ Child twelve days after His birth. For this reason, in many countries, gifts are exchanged on Twelfth Night (January 6) rather than on Christmas Day.

The word "magi" is of Indo-Germanic origin, meaning "great, illustrious." They were not kings. Popular tradition has conferred this title on them and, in the same way, established the "fact" that there were three Magi.

It is not certain whether the Magi came from Arabia, Iraq, Iran, Afghanistan, or India. It is known, however, that they were a highly esteemed class of priestly scholars who devoted themselves not only to religion but to the study of medicine, mathematics, natural sciences, astronomy, and astrology.

St. Bede the Venerable, in a retelling of the legend of the Magi in 735, says that the first was called Melchior, an old man with white hair and a long beard, who offered gold to the newborn King. The second was Gaspar, young and beardless and "of ruddy hue," who brought incense. The third was Baltasar, with heavy beard and black complexion. He carried myrrh, which "prefigured the death of the Son of man."

Popular tradition also says that Empress Helena, as the result of a vision, had the Magi's remains brought back to Byzantium. They were later removed to Milan, and in 1162 the skulls of the "three kings" were taken to Cologne where they are still enshrined.

Most authorities agree that the three ships of the song by that name are traditionally the ships by which they were brought to Cologne. The carol has simply transferred the ships from the Magi to Christ himself, which is typical of what the popular imagination has done with many folk carols.

No other story in the New Testament gives such opportunity for pageantry as the Magi scene. It was a story imbued with all the richness, romance, and "mystery" of the East. Some of this is revealed in the songs of the Magi.

We Three Kings

Words and music by John Henry Hopkins, Jr., 1820-91

1. We three kings of O - ri - ent are, Bear - ing
2. Born a King on Beth - le - hem's plain, Gold I

(Melchior):

gifts we trav - erse a - far, Field and foun - tain,
bring to crown Him a - gain, King for - ev - er,

moor and moun - tain, Fol - low - ing yon - der star.
ceas - ing nev - - er, O - ver us all to reign.

O, _____ star of won - der, star of night,

Star with roy - al beau - ty bright, West - ward lead - ing,

still pro - ceed - ing, Guide us to thy per - fect light.

3. *(Caspar):*
    Frankincense to offer have I,
    Incense owns a Deity nigh;
    Prayer and praising, all men raising,
    Worship Him, God on high. *(Refrain)*

4. *(Balthazar):*
    Myrrh is mine, its bitter perfume
    Breathes a life of gathering gloom;
    Sorrowing, sighing, bleeding, dying,
    Sealed in the stone-cold tomb. *(Refrain)*

5. *(All):*
    Glorious now behold Him arise,
    King and God and sacrifice;
    Alleluia, alleluia:
    Earth to the heavens replies. *(Refrain)*

THERE · WERE · THREE · KINGS

· DE · DRIE · KONINGEN ·

Moderately fast

Traditional Flemish from *Chants Populaires Flamands.*

1. There were three kings, on jour - ney did go, Led by a star through the cold
2. An an - gel came, to Jo - seph did say, "Oh, hur - ry to E - gypt! Go!

win - ter's deep snow. Joy - ful - ly they came on their way, ___ Search-
Please don't de - lay! Her - od comes near, ven - geance to reap, ___ So

ing for Him who was born King on that day. With drums and with trum-pets they
hur-ry now, has-ten, and, Ma-ry, don't weep!" On don-key they went with sweet

came on their way. With drums and with trum-pets they came on their way.
Je-sus a-sleep! Cra-dled by Ma-ry, sweet Je-sus did sleep.

3. To save Him then, to Egypt they went,
   Keeping our Saviour from such evil intent.
   Little ones all to death were sent;
   Oh, what heart could ever retell that event?
   To Him who was saved from King Herod's cruel men,
   To Him who was saved, we sing Noël again!

1. *Laatst waren er drie Koningen wijs*
   Zij reisden alover het sneeuwwit ijs
   Alover 't land gheel triomphant,
   Om Jesus te zoeken; dien weerdigen pand.
   Zij kwamen met ketels en trommelen aan,
   Zij kwamen met ketels en trommelen aan.

2. *De engel die sprak sint Joseph toe:*
   "Vlucht naar Egypten met Jesus zoet,"
   Herodes die kwam
   Met een groot gespan;
   De ezel die vluchtte,
   Maria die zuchtte,
   Sint Joseph die troostte z'in hare droefheid.

3. *Herodes ontbood kleen ende groot,*
   Alle die bloedjes ze slagen z'al dood.
   Wie heeft ooit gehoord
   Van zulk een moord?
   D'onnozel herten
   Vol herten en smerten
   Zij wierden in hunder bloed gesmoord.

65

HE IS BORN
W ZLOBIE LEZY

Polish, thirteenth century

1. In a man-ger He is ly-ing,
Let us go to greet the Child! Ba-by dar-ling, in-fant Je-sus,
Lit-tle Sav-iour sweet and mild! Bells are ring-ing, good news bring-ing!

2. While the shep-herds watch were keep-ing
O-ver sheep that star-ry night, An-gels came and brought good ti-dings
In a blaze of shin-ing light! All the shep-herds, gen-tly pip-ing,

Join the hap - py,   joy - ous sing - ing,   "He is born! Oh   Ho - ly Child!"
Ran to   see   Him,   soft - ly sing - ing,   "He is born! Oh   ho - ly night!"

poco rit.

3. Come, good people, follow after,
 Come and see the blessed Child!
 He is lying in a stable,
 Little Jesus, sweet and mild.
 Join the angels' happy singing!
 Hear the shepherds, nowells bringing!
 "He is born! The blessèd Child!"

Throughout France, Belgium, and middle Europe the dramatization of the story of the Magi was a customary feature of the Christmas celebration.

The three kings were frequently represented by three young boys who had been chosen by the local priest for their scholarship and character. In long, flowing robes, their heads high with the crowns they wore, they marched proudly through the town, gathering all the children as they went. Singing together, they finally arrived at the church. There, grouped around the altar cradle where the Child lay, they sang again before the midnight Mass was read.

Sometimes, as in Hungary, three young girls would portray the kings. Wearing tall white mitres and dressed in hand-embroidered, all-white dresses, they led the carol-singing procession to the church.

THE GOLDEN CAROL

Not too slowly

1. "The star we've wait-ed for so long To tell us of His com-ing, Is
2. "The way is long, the way is cold; We can-not tar-ry lon-ger. The

here! Is here! And we must go With trum - pets, and drums drum - ming! The
birth of Him the star has told; The way is still much lon - ger. A

star we fol - low on this night Will lead us to the cra - dle, Where
king is born this ho - ly morn, And gifts to Him we're bring - ing. The

He was born this ho - ly night, In poor and low - ly sta - ble."
Child we've wait - ed for is born! O hear the an - gels sing - ing!"

D. C.

3. And so three kings went on their way
   To greet the Holy Infant;
   They went on that first Christmas Day
   To honor Holy Infant.
   They called Him King of kings then,
   And knelt in adoration,
   For He had come to bring all men
   To love and peace, salvation.

Traditional English melody
These are new verses written for a traditional melody.

Twelfth Night Song

1. See them! There they go._ Three no-ble kings Go rid-ing through the snow._ Three kings_ on three_
2. Drums sound as they come,_ Joy-ful-ly ri - ding To_ see Ma- ry's_ Son, The_ new-born_

hor - ses_ Go trot-ting on their way To_ see Him, Je- su, born a King to - day.
King. To_ Beth- le - hem they come To_ see Him, Je- su, Ma-ry's new-born Son.

3. Furs they brought the Child,
   Furs, warm and soft,
   From forest wild.
   And gay songs to sing,
   To Him they did bring,
   To Him, to Jesu,
   Tiny little sweet boy Child.

4. O star, shining bright,
   That cold winter night,
   When three kings came
   Bearing gifts for the Child,
   Born that night of Mary,
   Sweet and mild,
   Mary, mother of the Child.

Melchior and Balthazar

Melchior et Balthazar

A French round from Bas-Languedoc

Not too fast

Mel - chi - or and Bal - tha - zar Came from A - fri -
Mel - chi - or et Bal - tha - zar Sont par - tis d'A -

ca, _____ Came from A - fri - ca; _____ Mel - chi - or and Bal - tha -
fri - que; Sont par - tis d'A - fri - que; Mel - chi - or et Bal - tha -

zar Came from A - fri - ca, oh yes, With King Gas - par!
zar Sont par - tis d'A - frique A - vec le roi Gas - pard!

2. When they came to Bethlehem,
They unpacked their hampers,
They unpacked their hampers;
When they came to Bethlehem,
They unpacked their hampers
And their mannequin!

3. Like three starved and hungry wolves,
They ate all their soup,
They ate all their soup;
Like three starved and hungry wolves,
They ate all their soup,
And it was cabbage soup!

2. *Arrivés à Béthléem,*
Ils défir' leur manne,
Ils défir' leur manne;
Arrivés à Béthléem,
Ils défir' leur manne
Et leur mannequin.

3. *Affamés comme des loups,*
Ils mangèr' la soupe,
Ils mangèr' la soupe;
Affamés comme des loups,
Ils mangèr' la soupe,
*Et la soupe aux choux!**

*If sung as a round, the second part should start with vs. 2.

Nativity

n that night so long ago, shepherds, tending their flocks on the slopes of the rocky ridge just outside Bethlehem, huddled close to their sheep. The wind blew bitter and cold, but they dared not sleep. They were keeping a special vigil that night. Sacrificial lambs would soon be needed for the Feast of Passover. Thinking of this long-anticipated feast, they pulled their worn cloaks closer and prayed for an early spring.

Life for these shepherds was austere and circumscribed—a circle defined by the seasons which made a calendar of days ordained by the Temple and conditioned by sheep. Like most Israelites under the rule of Caesar Augustus, these shepherds were poor and oppressed. There were no "unexpected" joys. The years followed one another with regimented sameness, the Temple providing the only embroidery on a life worked out in a small bare circle of space and time. When the angel appeared that night, so unexpectedly, these shepherds must surely have "trembled and shook in that heavenly light." But the angel said, "Do not fear, for I bring you good news of a great joy which is coming to all your people. For to you today in the city of David, a Saviour is born who is Christ the Lord."

The Gospel tells a simple story of the Nativity. It says that, in response to a decree issued by Caesar Augustus that a census of the whole world should be taken, Joseph left Nazareth and went with Mary to Bethlehem to register. While there, Mary brought forth her firstborn son, wrapped him in swaddling clothes, and laid him in a manger. An angel of the Lord had announced to shepherds abiding in the fields nearby the news of great joy, the shepherds came to the stable, saw the Child, and spread the news abroad. The rest of the story is as simply told.

Since that first telling, however, man has never ceased in his fashioning of endless variations. Not only with countless combinations of words, both spoken and written, but in stone and clay and paint, with song, with dance and with all types of drama, man has recreated, and continues still to recreate, the story of the Nativity.

The first hymns in honor of the Nativity were written in the fifth century, soon after Christmas was fully established as one of the great annual Church feasts. These were in Latin, however, and it was not until the thirteenth century, when St. Francis inspired his companions to write in the vernacular, that songs to celebrate the Nativity were written for the people to sing.

From Italy the carol spread rapidly to France and to Spain, to all Europe, and soon beautiful songs of the Nativity were springing up like wild flowers everywhere where people celebrated Christmas.

Songs of the Nativity are of all types, from true folk song to composed carols, and come from all periods of time, from the thirteenth century to the present.

JOY TO THE WORLD

Anonymous melody with words by Isaac Watts, 1674-1748.

sing, And — heav - en, and heav - en and na - ture sing.
joy, Re - peat, — re - peat ——— the sound - ing joy.

3. He rules the world with truth and grace,
   And makes the nations prove
   The glories of His righteousness,
   And wonders of His love,
   And wonders of His love,
   And wonders, and wonders of His love.

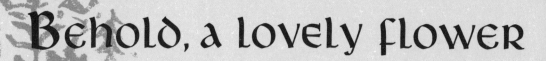

Behold, a lovely flower

es ist ein' ros' entsprungen

Fifteenth century words and melody from *Speierschen Gesangbuch*;
Cologne, 1600. Arrangement by Michael Praetorius from
Musae Sioniae, 1609.

2. It was Isaiah's promise,
   This flower blossoming;
   And Mary, Virgin Mother,
   To her we now do sing.
   Because God willed it so,
   Sweet Mary bore a Baby
   To save us all from woe.

3. Praise Him, the father holy,
   Praise Mary, sweet and mild,
   And praises sing to Him,
   The little tiny Child.
   Oh sing we now to Him;
   Oh holy, holy Infant,
   In our hearts, enter in.

2. *Das Röslein, dass ich meine,*
   Davon Jesaias sagt,
   Ist Maria die reine,
   Die uns dies Blümlein bracht;
   Aus Gottes ew'gem Rat
   Hat sie ein Kindlein g'boren,
   Ist blieb'n ein' reine Magd.

3. *Wir bitten dich von Herzen,*
   Maria, Rose zart,
   Durch dieses Blümlein's Schmerzen,
   Die er empfunden hat,
   Wollst uns behülflich sein,
   Dass wir ihm mögen machen
   Ein' Wohnung hübsch und fein!

Silent Night Stille Nacht

*The original setting for this song called for voices accompanied by the guitar.

Joseph Mohr, 1792-1848

Franz Gruber, 1787-1863

2. Silent night! Holy night!
   Shepherds quake at the sight;
   Glories stream from heaven afar,
   Heav'nly hosts sing alleluia;
   Christ the Saviour is born!
   Christ the Saviour is born!

2. *Stille Nacht! Heilige Nacht!*
   Hirten erst Kund gemacht;
   Durch der Engel Halleluja
   Tönt es laut von fern und nah:
   Christ, der Retter, ist da!
   Christ, der Retter, ist da!

THE CHILD JESUS

EL NIÑO JESÚS

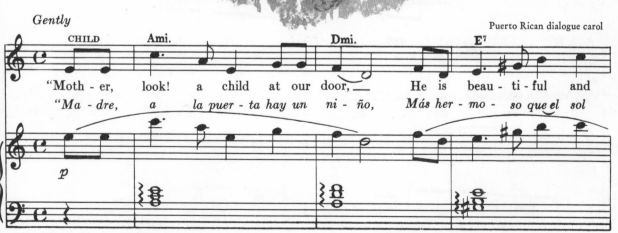

Gently

Puerto Rican dialogue carol

CHILD Ami.   Dmi.   E⁷

"Moth - er, look! a child at our door,— He is beau - ti - ful and

"Ma - dre, a la puer - ta hay un ni - ño, Más her - mo - so que el sol

This carol has been attributed to Antonio Machado, a well-known Spanish poet who wrote for the people in the people's idiom.

moth - er lives there too; _____ I came to earth to
ma - dre tam - - bien; _____ Yo ba - je a la

suf - fer, To __ bring His love to you!" _____
tier - ra Pa - ra pa - - de - - cer!" _____

2. When the Child had come and stood
   By the fire till He was warm,
   The mother asked what country
   Did He rule, where was He born?

3. "My Father is in heaven,
   My mother lives there too;
   I came to earth to suffer,
   To bring His love to you!"

2. *Entra el niño y se calienta*
   Y después de calentado
   La madre le pregunta
   De qué tierra es su reinado.

3. *"Mi padre es del cielo,*
   Mi madre tambien;
   Yo baje a la tierra
   Para padecer!"

MORNING SONG

French (Haut-Languedoc)

1. Lis - ten! Can't you hear the sing- ing, Sweet- ly sound-ing ear - ly morn; Gold- en
1. E - cou - tons donc les au - bades Qui vien - nent de ré - son - ner; Sur des

trum- pets clear - ly ring - ing, Tel - ling all a king is born! Trum- pet -
trom - pet - tes do - ré - es, Di - sent qu'un Dau - phin est né. L'u - ne

ing: Ta- ta - ra, ta - ta - ra- tam - poun, Ta - ra, ta - ta - ra - tam - poun! And then the
fait: Ta - ra - ra, Ta - ra - re - ro, Lin - tam-poun, La - de - ri - tam - poun! Et voi - ci

Écoutons donc les Aubades

o - ther trum - pets too: Ta - ta - ra, ta - ta - ra, ta - ta - ra - tam - poun! Ta-
l'au - tre qui ré - pond: Ta - ra - ra, ta - ra - ra, Ta - ra - re - ro! Lin - tam-

ra, ta - ta - ra - tam - poun! The new - born King, the sweet Je - su!
poun, La - de - ri - tam - poun! Nou - veau ve - nu, pe - tit pou - pon!

2. Taking off our hats, we enter
  Stable there to see Jesu:
  "Darling baby, we are singing
  Sweet and gay noëls for you!"
    We will play: Ta-ta-ra (etc.)
    And then another will play too:
      Ta-ta-ra (etc.)
    The newborn king, the sweet Jesu!

3. Silver flutes and golden trumpets,
  Drums and pipes and tinkling bells,
  Gayly now their music ringing,
  While the angels sing noëls!
    Sing to Him: Ta-ta-ra (etc.)
    And then each one will sing it too:
      Ta-ta-ra (etc.)
    The newborn king, the sweet Jesu!

2. *En entrant dedans l'étable,*
  Nous ôterons le chapeau
  Et dirons: Enfant aimable,
  Nous venons chanter Noël!
    Nous ferons: Ta-ra-ra (etc.)
    Un autre fera la répons:
      Ta-ra-ra (etc.)
    Nouveau venu, petit poupon!

3. *Sonnez, fifres et trompettes,*
  Timbales et chalumeaux!
  Et vous, les claires clochettes,
  Et le choeur des angelets!
    Dites lui: Ta-ra-ra (etc.)
    Et chacun vous fait le répons:
      Ta-ra-ra (etc.)
    Nouveau venu, petit poupon!

The First Nowell

There are many theories regarding the original of "The First Nowell," but mystery still surrounds it. It first appeared in print in 1822. This version is from Sandys' collection, 1833, but it is generally agreed that this carol cannot be later than the seventeenth century.

Traditional English

Not too slowly

1. The first Now-ell the an-gel did say Was to
2. They looked up and saw a star Shin-ing

cer-tain poor shep-herds in fields as they lay; In fields where
in the east, be-yond them far; And to the

they lay, keep-ing their sheep, On a cold win-ter's night that
earth it gave great light, And so it con-tin-ued both

was ___ so deep:
day ___ and night.   Now - ell, ___ Now - ell,   Now - ell,   Now -

ell,   Born   is   the   King ___ of   Is -   ra - el!

 3. And by the light of that same star,
    Three Wise Men came from country far;
    To seek for a king was their intent,
    And to follow the star wheresoever it went:
      (Refrain)

4. This star drew nigh to the northwest;
   O'er Bethlehem it took its rest,
   And there it did both stop and stay
   Right over the place where Jesus lay:
    (Refrain)

7. Between an ox-stall and an ass
   This child truly there born he was;
   For want of clothing they did him lay
   All in the manger, among the hay:
    (Refrain)

5. Then did they know assuredly
   Within that house the King did lie:
   One entered in then for to see,
   And found the babe in poverty:
    (Refrain)

8. Then let us all with one accord
   Sing praises to our heavenly Lord,
   That hath made heaven and earth of naught,
   And with his blood mankind hath bought:
    (Refrain)

6. Then entered in those Wise Men three,
   Fell reverently upon their knee,
   And offered there in his presènce
   Both gold and myrrh and frankincense:
    (Refrain)

9. If we in our time shall do well,
   We shall be free from death and hell;
   For God hath preparèd for us all
   A resting place in general:
    (Refrain)

Hark ✝✝✝ The Herald Angels Sing

Charles Wesley

W. H. Cummings

1. Hark! the her - ald an - gels sing, __ "Glo - ry to the new - born King;
2. Christ, by high - est heaven a - dored, __ Christ, the ev - er - last - ing Lord,

Peace on earth, and mer - cy mild, __ God and sin - ners rec - on - ciled!"
Late in time be - hold Him come, __ Off - spring of a vir - gin's womb.

3. Hail, the heaven-born Prince of Peace!
Hail, the Sun of Righteousness!
Light and life to all He brings,
Risen with healing in His wings.
Mild He lays His glory by,
Born that man no more may die,
Born to raise the sons of earth,
Born to give them second birth. *(Refrain)*

This carol is an adaptation of a chorus from Mendelssohn's secular cantata, "Festgesang," made by Cummings in 1856 as a setting for the hymn written by Charles Wesley more than a century earlier.

IT CAME
UPON A MIDNIGHT CLEAR

Edmund H. Sears, 1810-1876

Richard S. Willis, 1819-1900

1. It came up-on ___ a mid-night clear, That glo-rious song ___ of
2. Still through the clo-ven skies they come, With peace-ful wings ___ un-

old, _____ From an-gels bend---ing near the earth To
furled, _____ And still their heav-en-ly mu-sic floats O'er

3. O ye, beneath life's crushing load
   Whose forms are bending low,
   Who toil along the climbing way,
   With painful steps and slow,
   Look now, for glad and golden hours
   Come swiftly on the wing;
   O rest beside the weary road
   And hear the angels sing!

4. For lo, the days are hastening on,
   By prophets seen of old,
   When with the ever-circling years
   Shall come the time foretold,
   When the new heaven and earth shall own
   The Prince of Peace their King,
   And the whole world send back the song
   Which now the angels sing.

Blessed be that maid Marie

Old English carol

Melody from William Ballet's *Lute Book*

Not too slowly

1. Bles - sed be that Maid Ma - rie; _____
2. In a man - ger of an __ ass _____

Born __ He was of __ her __ bo - dy;
Je - su __ lay and __ lul - lèd __ was;

Ve - ry __ God ere __ time __ be - gan,
Born __ to __ die up - on __ the __ tree

*Latin translations: Refrain: *Jesus is born today of the Virgin.* V. 2. For sinful man. V. 3. Glory in the highest. V. 4. On which Christ was born. In V. 4. "Assoil" *means procure our forgiveness.*

92

The veneration of Mary was one of the most magnificent and potent forces in medieval religion. Many carols were written in praise of her, some of which date back to the twelfth and thirteenth centuries—to the days of troubadors and minnesingers, to the time when knights often dedicated their lives to her.

3. Sweet and blissful was the song
   Chanted of the angel throng,
   Peace on earth, Alléluya.
   In excelsis gloria. *(Refrain)*

4. Make we merry on this fest,
   In quo Christus natus est;
   On this Child I pray you call
   To assoil and save us all. *(Refrain)*

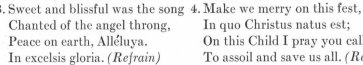

93

O Little Town of Bethlehem

Phillips Brooks, 1835-1893

Lewis H. Redner, 1831-1908

Not too slowly

1. O lit-tle town of Beth-le-hem, How still we see thee lie! A-bove thy deep and dream-less sleep The si-lent stars go by; Yet in thy dark streets shin-eth The ev-er-last-ing Light; The

2. For Christ is born of Ma-ry, And gath-ered all a-bove, While mor-tals sleep, the an-gels keep Their watch of won-d'ring love. O morn-ing stars, to-geth-er Pro-claim the ho-ly birth, And

BETHLEHEM

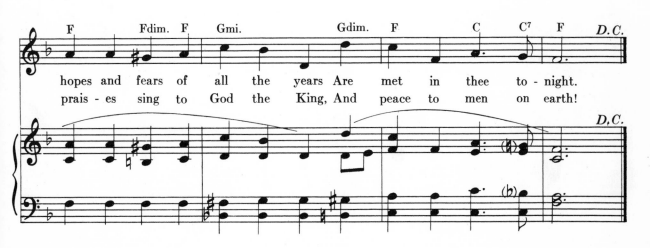

hopes and fears of all the years Are met in thee to - night.
prais - es sing to God the King, And peace to men on earth!

3. How silently, how silently,
   The wondrous gift is giv'n!
   So God imparts to human hearts
   The blessings of His heav'n.
   No ear may hear His coming,
   But in this world of sin,
   Where meek souls will receive Him still,
   The dear Christ enters in.

4. O holy Child of Bethlehem,
   Descend to us, we pray;
   Cast out our sin and enter in;
   Be born in us today!
   We hear the Christmas angels
   The great glad tidings tell;
   O come to us, abide with us
   Our Lord Emmanuel!

O come, all ye faithful
Adeste, fideles

Words and music by J. F. Wade, c. 1711-86

Majestically

1. O come, all ye faith - ful, Joy - ful and tri - um - phant, O
2. God of God, Light of Light,

come ye, O come ye to Beth - le - hem;
Lo! He ab - hors not the Vir - gin's womb;

Come and be - hold Him, Born the King of An - - gels: O
Ver - y _____ God, Be - got - ten, not cre - a - - ted.

Refrain

come let us a - dore Him, O come let us a - dore Him, O

come let us a - dore Him, ___ Christ _____ the Lord.

D.S. %

D.S. %

3. Sing, choirs of Angels,
   Sing in exultation,
   Sing, all ye citizens of heaven above;
   Glory to God
   In the highest: *(Refrain)*

4. Yea, Lord, we greet Thee,
   Born this happy morning,
   Jesu, to Thee be glory given;
   Word of the Father,
   Now in flesh appearing: *(Refrain)*

In a pamphlet which is considered the classic source of information about this hymn, Dom John Stéphan of Buckfast Abbey proves, on manuscript evidence, that both words and tune are the composition of J. F. Wade, an Englishman who worked all his life as a copyist and music teacher at Douay, a renowned Roman Catholic center in France. Wade's original manuscript is dated 1751, but the tune in the rhythm with which we are familiar comes from a manuscript dated 1760. This translation was made by Reverend Francis Oakeley in 1841.

Legendary Carols

The Legendary Carols like the whole treasury of folk-tales surrounding the story of the Nativity, sprang from the fertile imagination of the people—an imagination uninhibited for the most part by formal learning and nourished to a large extent by superstition and dimly remembered pre-Christian beliefs.

One of the characteristics of this type of carol is the way in which it usually reveals its geographic or ethnic origin. From southern countries come carols telling of birds and flowers that guard the Babe. Farther north, the fir tree and the snow appear. In lands facing the sea there are songs of Christmas ships, and from the hill towns, stories of shepherds and surefooted animals. In many of these carols the birds, animals, and bees speak and sing, trees leaf and flowers blossom in the snows of winter. Some tell of elfin beings, like the trolls and tomtar of Sweden. Some are the retelling in new guise of ancient fertility legends. Some are simply imaginative reconstructions of the childhood of Christ.

Some of these carols recount the deeds and miracles of men like St. Nicholas, who must surely have been the hardest working saint of all. Actually a fourth century bishop of Myra in Asia Minor, St. Nicholas eventually became the patron saint of sailors (and later of all travelers), the special guardian of unmarried girls, and the protector of little children everywhere. In some countries, such as Russia, he became the special saint of the country itself.

Some of the legends attached to the saint have had curious applications. For instance, because it was said that "a man's goods are safe under the sign of St. Nicholas," his three bags of gold (with which he is usually pictured and which eventually assumed the shape of balls) have become the symbol of the pawnbroker.

After many years, in which pre-Christian folk beliefs and religious teachings were blended, St. Nicholas emerged as the bearer of gifts, and his day, December 6, remains for much of Europe the most distinctive children's festival of the year. In America, where he was brought by the Dutch, he evolved into the folk figure we call Santa Claus and, through the influence of the English, he arrives here not on the eve of December 6 but on the eve of December 25.

Legendary carols are often pure folk song (songs, transmitted orally, with anonymous authors) but there are some, notably "Good King Wenceslas" and "A Visit from St. Nicholas," both written in comparatively modern times, which, from the purist's standpoint, are not folk song since we happen to know who wrote them. Whatever the type, however, all legendary carols are alike in one respect. They all tell a story.

CAROL OF THE BIRDS

Czech

Moderately fast

mp   l.h.

G

1. From
(2. A)

out of a wood ___ a cuck-oo did fly, Cuck-oo! He
pi - geon flew o - ver to Gal - - i - lee, Coo ___ He

ver-croo

came to a man - ger with joy - ful cry, Cuck - oo. He
strut - ted, and cooed, and was full of glee, Coo ___ And

ver-croo

3. A dove settled down upon Nazareth,
   Tsucroo,
   And tenderly chanted with all his breath,
   Tsucroo;
   "O you," he cooed, "so good and true,
   My beauty do I give to you—
   Tsucroo, tsucroo, tsucroo."

Carol of the Birds

Le Noël des Oiseaux

French (Haut-Languedoc)

1. See how the No - ël star shines bright! But what is that I hear to - night? A flock of lit - tle birds, it's true, Fly - ing to Beth - l'em two by two.

1. Voi - ci l'é - toi - le de No - ël, Quel est ce bruit sur la mai - son? C'est u - ne trou - pe d'oi - se - lets, A Beth-lé - em vont deux à deux.

2. In stable bare lies baby sweet;
   Brown ox and donkey guard his sleep.
   Why, little birds, did you come too?
   "We bring love to Him, Jesu."

3. Up from the hay, flew rooster old,
   Up to the rack, he flew most bold,
   Crowing a blessing clear and true,
   Crowing so clear: "Coucouroucou!"

4. Down from his nest the goldfinch flew,
   Bowed and said: "Tirli, chiu, chiu!"
   "Chiu, chiu!" replied the sparrow small,
   And the quail called: "Palpabat-bal!"

5. Whistling lightly, blackbird comes,
   While the linnet softly hums;
   Pigeon calls: "Roucou, roucou!"
   And the lark sings: "Tirolirou!"

6. Perching beside the greenfinch small,
   Wagtail does sing and sweetly call;
   While nightingale up in the tree
   Sings to the Child: "La sol fa mi!"

7. To honor Him, the child Jesu,
   Angels and shepherds, sweet birds too,
   Come and adore Him, your love tell;
   Sing Noël! Noël! Noël!

2. *Dans l'étable où le Roi du Ciel*
   Dort entre l'âne et le boeuf brun,
   Pourquoi venez-vous donc, oiseaux?
   "Nous venons pour adorer Dieu!"

3. *Le coq s'avance le permier,*
   Et monte sur le râtelier,
   Puis, pour commencer l'oraison,
   Il entonn' son: "Coucouroucou!"

4. *Le chardonn'ret sort de son nid,*
   Salue et dit: "Tirli, chiu, chiu!"
   "Chiu, chiu!" répond le passereau,
   Et la caille fait: "Palpabat!"

5. *Le merle arrive en sifflotant,*
   Et le linot en chantonnant;
   Le pigeon fait: "Roucou, roucou!"
   Et l'alouett': "Tirolirou!"

6. *La bergeronnette, à son tour,*
   Se pose a côté du verdier,
   Et, sur l'arbre, le rossignol
   Chante à l'Enfant: "Ré mi fa sol!"

7. *Pour honorer le fils de Dieu,*
   Venez en grande dévotion,
   Anges, bergers, oiseaux, du Ciel,
   Chantez Noël! Noël! Noël!

JOSEPH and MARY

Parallel stories concerning the gift of a cherry (or other fruit carrying its own seed) occur in Finnish epic poetry and Mexican mythology, in Egyptian, Arab, and numerous other sources. The legend as it is told here is a combination of ancient fertility legends and one of the infancy miracle stories in the Apocryphal New Testament. This is a very popular carol in England, where it is known as "The Cherry Tree Carol" or "As Joseph was A-Walking."

Lyrics from Kentucky

Traditional English

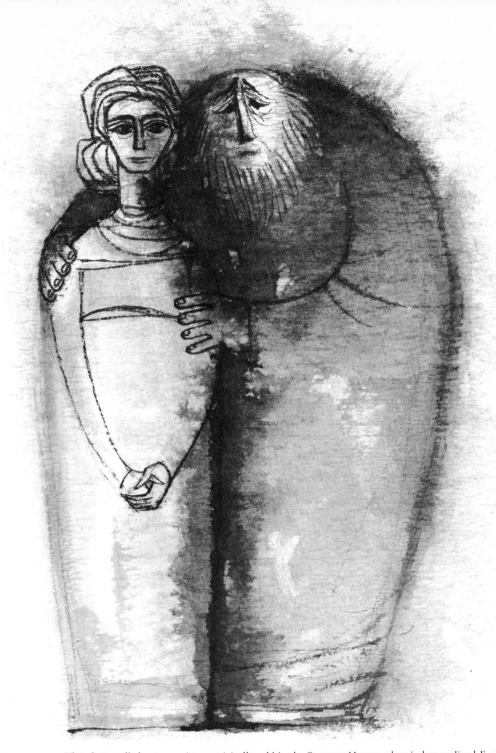

These lyrics tell the story as it was originally told in the Coventry Mystery plays in late medieval England.*

3. Then Joseph flew in anger,
 In anger flew he,
 "Let the father of the Baby
 Gather cherries for thee."

4. Then Jesus spoke a few words,
 A few words spoke he,
 "Give my mother some cherries,
 Bow down, cherry tree!"

5. "Bow down, o cherry tree,
 Low down to the ground!"
 Then Mary gathered cherries
 And Joseph stood around.

6. Then Joseph took Mary
 All on his right knee,
 "What have I done, Lord?
 Have mercy on me."

7. Then Joseph took Mary
 All on his left knee,
 "Oh tell me, little Baby,
 When will thy birthday be?"

8. "The sixth of January,
 My birthday will be,
 When the stars in the sky
 Will tremble with glee."

*From the Archive of American Folk Song (AAFS 1010 A1, Library of Congress).

The Friendly Beasts~~~~~

English--Twelfth Century

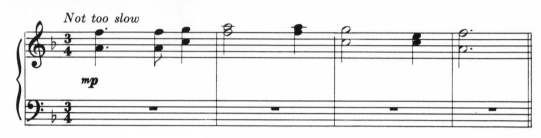

Not too slow

mp

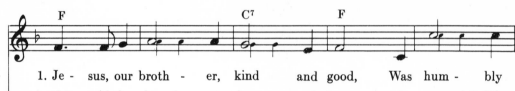

F   C⁷   F

1. Je - sus, our broth - er, kind   and good,   Was hum - bly
2. "I,"   said the don - key, all shag - gy and brown,   "I   car - ried His

B♭   C⁷   F   Gmi.

born in a   sta - ble rude. The friend - ly beasts a -
moth - er up - hill and down, I   car - ried her safe - ly to

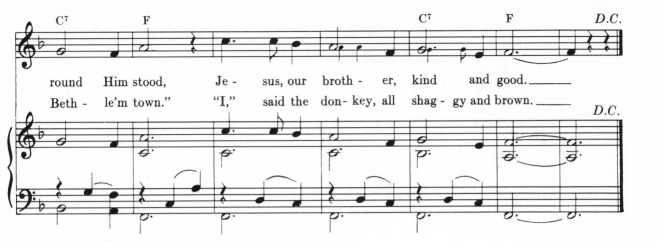

round Him stood, Je- sus, our broth- er, kind and good. _____

Beth- le'm town." "I," said the don- key, all shag- gy and brown. _____

D.C.

3

"I," said the cow, all white and red,
"I gave Him my manger for a bed,
I gave Him my hay to pillow His head."
"I," said the cow, all white and red.

4

"I," said the sheep with the curly horn,
"I gave Him my wool for a blanket warm,
He wore my coat on Christmas morn."
"I," said the sheep with the curly horn.

5

"I," said the dove from the rafters high,
"I cooed Him to sleep so He would not cry,
We cooed Him to sleep, my mate and I."
"I," said the dove from the rafters high.

6

So every beast, by some good spell,
In the stable rude was glad to tell
Of the gift he gave Immanuel,
The gift he gave Immanuel.

I saw three ships

Not too quickly

Traditional English

1. I saw three ships come sail - ing in, On Christ - mas Day, on Christ - mas Day, I saw three ships come sail - ing in, On Christ - mas Day in the morn - ing.

2. And what was in those ships all three? On Christ - mas Day, on Christ - mas Day, And what was in those ships all three? On Christ - mas Day in the morn - ing.

A very popular carol, this appeared in various versions in all the broadsides of England. A true folk carol, "Three Ships" is anonymous and of uncertain origin and date. Charming and ingenuous, it is universally appealing.

3. 'Twas Joseph and his Fair Ladye,
   On Christmas Day, on Christmas Day,
   'Twas Joseph and his Fair Ladye,
   On Christmas Day in the morning.

4. O, he did whistle and she did sing,
   On Christmas Day, on Christmas Day,
   O, he did whistle and she did sing,
   On Christmas Day in the morning.

5. Saint Michael was the steeres-man,
   On Christmas Day, on Christmas Day,
   Saint Michael was the steeres-man,
   On Christmas Day in the morning.

6. Pray, whither sailed those ships all three?
   On Christmas Day, on Christmas Day,
   Pray, whither sailed those ships all three?
   On Christmas Day in the morning.

7. O, they sailed into Bethlehem,
   On Christmas Day, on Christmas Day,
   O, they sailed into Bethlehem,
   On Christmas Day in the morning.

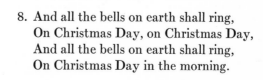

8. And all the bells on earth shall ring,
   On Christmas Day, on Christmas Day,
   And all the bells on earth shall ring,
   On Christmas Day in the morning.

The Boar's Head Carol

This famous carol from the Middle Ages is still sung at Christmas dinner in the Queen's College, Oxford, as the boar's head is brought in with great ceremony.

Traditional English

1. The boar's head in hand bear I, Be-deck'd with bays and rose-ma-ry. And I pray you, mas-ters, be mer-ry. *Quot es-tis in con-vi-vi-o.*

2. The boar's head, as I un-der-stand, Is the brav-est dish in all the land, When thus be-deck'd with a gay gar-land, Let us *ser-vi-re can-ti-co.*

Refrain

Ca-put a-pri de-fe-ro, Red-dens lau-des Dom-i-no.

3. Our steward hath provided this,
In honour of the King of bliss,
Which on this day to be servèd is,
In Reginensi Atrio. (Refrain)

Latin translations: Refrain: *A boar's head I bear / Giving praises to the Lord.* V. 1. *Whoever at the feast may be.* V. 2. *Let us serve with song.* V. 3. *In the royal hall.*

How To Serve Up Boar's Head

"At Christmas time be careful of your Fame,
See the old Tenant's table be the same;
Then if you wou'd send up the Brawner's Head,
Sweet Rosemary and Bays around it spread:
His foaming tusks let some large Pippin grace,
Or 'midst these thund'ring Spears an Orange place,
Sauce, like himself, offensive to its Foes,
The Roguish Mustard, dang'rous to the Nose.
Sack, and well-spic'd Hippocras the Wine,
Wassail the Bowl with antient Ribbands fine,
Porridge with Plumbs, and Turkeys with the Chine."

(William King's *Art of Cookery,* 1663-1712.)

OLD ENGLISH VERSION

Burden: Caput apri refero
Resonens laudes Domino.

1. *The boris hed in hondes I brynge,*
   With garlondes gay and byrdes syngynge;[1]
   I pray you all, helpe me to synge,
   Qui estis in convivio. (Burden)

2. *The boris hede, I vnderstond,*
   Ys cheff seruyce in all this londe;
   Whersoever it may be fonde,
   Seruitur cum sinapio. (Burden)

3. *The boris hede, I dare well say,*
   Anon after the Twelfth Day[2]
   He taketh his leve and goth away,
   Exiuit tunc de patria. (Burden)

[1] This may mean an actual garnishing with captive live birds,
   a practice not too elaborate for Tudor feasts.
[2] In the manuscript "twelfth" is xiith.

x

Good ✳ King ✳ Wenceslas

The original song found with this melody in *Piae Cantiones*✳ was a thirteenth century spring song, *Tempus Adest Floridum*.

J. M. Neale (1818-1866)

✳*Piae Cantiones, 1582*

With movement

1. Good King Wen - ces - las looked out, On the Feast of Ste - phen,
2. "Hith - er, page, and stand by me, If thou know'st it, tell - ing,

When the snow lay round a - bout, Deep, and crisp, and e - ven;
Yon - der peas - ant, who is he? Where and what his dwell - ing?"

Bright - ly shone the moon that night, Though the frost was cru - el,
"Sire, he lives a good league hence, Un - der - neath the moun - tain,

When a poor man came in sight, Gather - ing win - ter fu - - el.
Right a - gainst the for - est fence, By Saint Ag - nes' foun - - tain."

3. "Bring me flesh, and bring me wine,
 Bring me pine-logs hither:
Thou and I will see him dine,
 When we bear them thither."
Page and monarch, forth they went,
 Forth they went together;
Through the rude wind's wild lament
 And the bitter weather.

4. "Sire, the night is darker now,
 And the wind blows stronger;
Fails my heart, I know not how;
 I can go no longer."
"Mark my footsteps, my good page;
 Tread thou in them boldly;
Thou shalt find the winter's rage
 Freeze thy blood less coldly."

5. In his master's steps he trod,
 Where the snow lay dinted;
Heat was in the very sod
 Which the Saint had printed.
Therefore, Christian men, be sure,
 Wealth or rank possessing,
Ye who now will bless the poor,
 Shall yourselves find blessing.

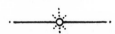

Wenceslas was duke of Bohemia during the tenth century. A fervent Christian, he had imported clergy, books, and relics from Germany to aid him in the Christianization of his duchy. In 929 he was murdered by his brother, Boleslav I, who then succeeded to the throne. Wenceslas was later sainted, but it was Rev. Neale's carol that brought the "Good King" a late but great renown.

The Holy Well

A very popular ballad-carol in all parts of England, this was a favorite of the minstrels who probably took it from a late medieval sermon. This is how the friars must have preached to the people, for this is the kind of thing that appealed and was remembered. In this song, the mother of Jesus is portrayed as a typical, sharp-tongued, busy housewife but, like all mothers, affectionate and protective; and Jesus, in spite of his holiness, is made a young boy with human desires and vulnerability.

Traditional English

Briskly

1. As it fell out __ one May morn - ing, On a bright hol - i -
2. Sweet Je - sus went down to yon - der town, As far as the Ho - ly

day, Sweet Je - sus asked His moth - er __ dear If He might go to
Well, And there did see as fine __ chil - dren As an - y tongue can

play. "To play, to play, sweet Je - sus, __ go, And to play now get you
tell. He said: "God bless you eve - ry __ one; May __ Christ your por - tion

gone, And let me hear __ of no com-plaints, At night when you come home."
be. Lit -tle chil - dren, shall __ I play with you? And you shall play with Me."

3. But they made answer to Him, "No."
   They were lords' and ladies' sons;
   And He, the meanest of them all,
   Was born in an ox's stall.
     Sweet Jesus turned Him around,
     And He neither laughed nor smiled,
     But the tears came trickling from His eyes
     Like water from the skies.

4. Sweet Jesus turned Him about,
   To His mother's dear home went He,
   And said, "I've been in yonder town,
   As after you may see.
     I've been in yonder town,
     As far as the Holy Well;
     There did I meet as fine children
     As any tongue can tell."

5. "I bid God bless them every one,
   And Christ their bodies see;
   Little children, shall I play with you?
   And you shall play with me.
     But then they answered me 'No,'
     They were lords' and ladies' sons;
     And I, the meanest of them all,
     Was born in an ox's stall."

6. "Though you are but a maiden's child,
   Born in an ox's stall,
   Thou art the Christ, the King of Heav'n,
   And the Saviour of them all.
     Sweet Jesus, go down to yonder town,
     As far as the Holy Well,
     And take away those sinful souls,
     And dip them deep in hell."

7. "Nay, nay," sweet Jesus mildly said,
   "Nay, nay, that must not be;
   For there are too many sinful souls
   Crying out for the help of me."
     O then bespoke the Angel Gabriel,
     "Upon our good St. Stephen,
     Although you are but a maiden's child,
     You are the King of Heav'n."

STEFAN WAS A STABLE BOY

Traditional Swedish

1. Ste - fan was a sta - ble - boy, We thank him now to - night. ____ He wa - ters his good hors - es five To fol - low star so bright. ____ Through the night so dark and cold, All the stars kept twink - ling, shin - ing bright. ____

2. Red were two of Ste - fan's hors - es, Rid - ing out so spright - ly; They knew that they must fol - low now The star that shone so bright - ly. Of five hors - es, two were white That went rid - ing out that star - ry night. ____

STAFFAN VAR EN STALLEDRÄNG

Staffan was an eleventh century Swedish missionary about whom many folk songs have been written. When he was killed by pagans who lived in the north, his body was strapped to the back of an unbroken foal which never halted until it reached Norrala, Staffan's home. Not only in Sweden, but in all Germanic lands, Staffan (Stephen) eventually became the patron saint of horses and of health. As the song notes, the Staffan here is confused with St. Stephen of Jerusalem and, together with him, is honored on December 26. On this day the people drink a "Stephen-Cup" to good health, although the older customs of racing horses and riding in procession around the churches and through the villages are no longer practiced.

3. Of five horses, one was grey,
   That one did Stefan ride;
   He carried Stefan all the way,
   He was good Stefan's guide.
   Stefan rode the dapple-grey
   All that long, dark, cold and wintry way.

4. Stefan rode and traveled far
   With horses five that night;
   He rode and came to Bethlehem
   Where shone the star so bright.
   There in stable lay the Child,
   Born of virgin maid so sweet and mild.

5. Stefan left then Bethlehem,
   To Herod he went riding;
   To tell the king a Child was born
   Who would be king of all men.
   Herod then in anger flew,
   Raged and stormed and said it was not true.

6. "If this roasted cock will crow
   Three times, then I'll believe you."
   He said, "Old rooster, rise and crow,
   Oh, crow if this be true."
   And that rooster on the plate
   Rose and crowed as rooster crows at daybreak!

7. Drink to Stefan this good Yule,
   Oh drink a Stefan-cup;
   To joy and love for all good men,
   To rooster too who rose up,
   And to horses five who went
   Following the star with good St. Stefan.

CAROLS OF CUSTOM

The customs of many peoples, many cultures and other religions have all helped to shape the celebration of Christmas as we know it today. And, when we sing, our caroling is merely a later expression of the same emotion that caused the Romans and other ancient peoples to sing hymns of joy to the returning spring, and a borrowing from the Hebrews, who were commanded to "serve the Lord with gladness, and come before his presence with a song."

The yule log and the mistletoe of England date back to the time of the Druids. Because the mistletoe was sacred to the Druids, who were the priests or ministers of religion of the ancient Britons and Gauls, the Church labeled it a "heathenish" plant but was unable to banish it completely. It ended up hanging in the kitchens, and later in the parlors, for kissing. A berry plucked for each kiss taken was the rule. When all the berries were gone, so were the kisses.

Decking the halls with boughs of holly and other evergreens comes to us from the Hebrews, Egyptians, Romans, and other ancient peoples for whom the evergreens were symbolic of life triumphant over death.

The wreath came originally from the ivy crown worn in festivals devoted to Bacchus. The holly wreath, with its prickles and blood-red berries, later became symbolic, for many Christians, of Christ's crown of thorns.

The still-prevalent custom in many countries of giving presents on New Year's Day dates back to antiquity—to the early Persians (who gave gilded eggs, an egg symbolizing the beginning of things), to the Chinese, and to many other peoples. In Rome, presents *(strenae)* were exchanged between friends and relatives and given to the emperor. In the beginning, apparently, *strenae* were twigs plucked from the grove of the goddess Strenia, who was associated with Janus in this feast, but later *strenae* became varied and many. Men gave honeyed things that the year of the recipient might be full of sweetness; lamps that it might be full of light; copper, silver, and gold, that wealth might flow in.

Throughout history "breaking bread together" has traditionally meant "peace" for men of all cultures. Quite naturally, then, the beginning of a new year became the time when family or clan and friends feasted together as a symbol of kinship or friendship. Today, although the original meaning has been generally forgotten, the tradition of "feasting together" is still carried on.

"Wassail" was the old Anglo-Saxon drinking pledge *Waes-Hael* which means "Be in health." At early Saxon feasts it was customary to drink a wassail to the lord, and thus the wassail bowl became a feature of the English Christmas and is kept filled, even today, from Christmas Eve to Twelfth Night.

Wishes for a good, a happy new year seems to be an almost universal custom, varying only in ways of expression. In Scotland, at the stroke of midnight on New Year's Eve, it was once customary to "perform a genteel dance" around the table while chanting:

"Weel may we a' be;
Ill may we never see,
Here's to the king
And the guid companie!"

At one time or another most of these customs have found expression in song.

Jeannette, Isabella

 Un Flambeau, Jeannette, Isabelle

Hanukkah, the Jewish "Festival of Lights," has strongly influenced the celebration of Christmas in Provence and other southern European regions.

Translated by E. Cuthbert Nunn (1868-1914)

French (possibly seventeenth century Provence)

1. Bring a torch, — Jean - nette, Is - a - bel - la! Bring a torch, to the cra - dle run! It is Je - sus, good folk of the vil - lage, Christ — is born and Ma - ry's call - ing,

1. Un flam - beau, — Jean - nette, Is - a - bel - le, Un flam - beau, — cou - rons au ber - ceau! C'est Jé - sus, bon - nes gens du — ha - meau, Le Christ est né, Ma - rie ap - pel - le,

Ah! ah! beau-ti-ful is the Moth-er!
Ah! Ah! que ___ la mère est bel - le,

Ah! ah! beau-ti-ful is her Son! _____
Ah! ah! ah! que l'En - fant est beau! _____

2. It is wrong when the Child is sleeping,
It is wrong to talk so loud.
Silence, all, as you gather around,
Lest your noise should waken Jesus:
Hush! Hush! see how fast He slumbers;
Hush! Hush! see how fast He sleeps!

3. Softly to the little stable,
Softly for a moment come!
Look and see how charming is Jesus,
How He is white, His cheeks are rosy!
Hush! Hush! see how the Child is sleeping;
Hush! Hush! see how He smiles in dreams!

2. *C'est un tort quand l'Enfant sommeille,*
C'est un tort de crier si fort.
Taisez-vous, l'un et l'autre, d'abord!
Au moindre bruit, Jésus s'éveille.
Chut! chut! chut! Il dort à merveille,
Chut! chut! chut! voyez comme Il dort!

3. *Doucement, dans l'étable close,*
Doucement, venez un moment!
Approchez, que Jésus est charmant!
Comme Il est blanc, comme Il est rose!
Do! Do! Do! que l'Enfant répose!
Do! Do! Do! qu'Il rit en dormant!

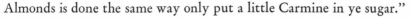

To Scorch Chesnutts

"Take yor Chesnutts and put them in a close oven to take off the Husks, then take a little loafe sugar in powder and a little water, and boyle to a Candy, take care it does not burn, then put in yor Chesnutts and stir it about in the Sugar till it stick on yor Chesnutts, and put them on a stone.

Almonds is done the same way only put a little Carmine in ye sugar."

"Curious Old Cookery Receipts," seventeenth century.

DECK THE HALLS

Decorating with evergreens and fragrant herbs is an ancient custom—a ceremony almost too old to be remembered as having a beginning.

Traditional Welsh

With spirit

1. Deck the halls with boughs of hol - ly, Fa la la la la, la la la la!
2. See the blaz - ing yule be - fore us,

'Tis the sea - son to be jol - ly, Fa la la la la, la la la la!
Strike the harp and join the cho - rus,

3. Fast away the old year passes,
    Fa la la la la, la la la la!
Hail the new, ye lads and lasses,
    Fa la la la la, la la la la!
Sing we joyous all together,
    Fa la la la la la, la la la!
Heedless of the wind and weather,
    Fa la la la la, la la la la!

Don we now our gay ap-par-el, Fa la la la la la, la la la!
Fol-low me in mer-ry meas-ure,

Troll the an-cient yule-tide car-ol, Fa la la la la, la la la la!
While I tell of yule-tide treas-ure!

Oh Christmas Tree

Oh Tannenbaum

Traditional German

Moderately

O Tan - nen-baum, O Tan - nen-baum, How love - ly are your branch- es!
O Tan - nen-baum, O Tan - nen-baum, Wie treu sind dei - ne Blät - ter!

In beau - ty green will al - ways grow Through sum-mer sun and win - ter snow. O
Du grünst nicht nur zur Som-mers- zeit Nein, auch im Win - ter, wenn es schneit. O

Tan - nen-baum, O Tan - nen-baum, How love - ly are your branch - es!
Tan - nen-baum, O Tan - nen-baum, Wie treu sind dei - ne Blät - ter!

The worship of trees dates back to the time when the world was peopled with wandering tribes. When the tribe moved on to a new settlement, they always left a group of trees in the center of the land they cleared. The central tree of this group was called the "mother tree." Here lived the ancestral spirits, and all religious ritual centered around it. From this ancient realm of tree worship comes the custom of the yule log. Eventually trees took on the form of deities, some of which were guardians of fertility. "Wassailing the trees" probably stems from this belief.

Our Christmas tree, although its roots are probably in these ancient folk customs, has a recognizable origin in the Paradise tree of the German medieval Mystery plays. This *Paradeisbaum*, a fir tree hung with apples and ringed with lighted candles, represented the Garden of Eden in the scene with Adam and Eve. When the Church did away with the Mysteries, the people took the tree, which had become the symbol of the Saviour, into their homes. In the fifteenth century, small white wafers, representing the Holy Eucharist, were hung on the tree along with the apples, and soon cookies in the shape of stars, angels, animals and birds were added to delight the children. Lights did not appear until the latter half of the seventeenth century. In the eighteenth century the Christmas tree spread first to Scandinavia, then to France, to England, and to America where it is now the most beloved feature of the Christmas celebration.

(First two lines of each stanza to be repeated.)

2.

O Tannenbaum, O Tannenbaum,
You are the tree most loved!
How often you give us delight
In brightly shining Christmas light!
O Tannenbaum, O Tannenbaum,
You are the tree most loved!

2.

O Tannenbaum, O Tannenbaum,
Du kannst mir sehr gefallen!
Wie oft hat nicht zur Weihnachtszeit
Ein Baum von dir mich hoch erfreut!
O Tannenbaum, O Tannenbaum,
Du kannst mir sehr gefallen!

3.

O Tannenbaum, O Tannenbaum,
Your beauty green will teach me
That hope and love will ever be
The way to joy and peace for me.
O Tannenbaum, O Tannenbaum,
Your beauty green will teach me.

3.

O Tannenbaum, O Tannenbaum,
Dein Kleid soll mich was lehren!
Die Hoffnung und Beständigkeit
Gibt Trost und Kraft zu aller Zeit.
O Tannenbaum, O Tannenbaum,
Dein Kleid soll mich was lehren!

HERE'S TO THEE, OLD APPLE TREE!

Traditional English (Sussex air)

Strongly

Here's to thee, old ap - ple tree, Here's ___ to thee, ___ old ap - ple tree!

1. Well may'st thou bud, And well may'st thou blow, And well may'st thou bear ___ Of ap ples e - now! Hats full! Caps full!

2. Give us a crop Of good ap - ples ripe, Red and well - roun - ded The good jui - cy type!

D.C.

Good bush - el - sacks full! My pock - ets too, Hur - rah! Was - sail!

3. Here is our ale,
Now drink of it well,
And give us good apples
Of which we can tell!

The custom of wassailing the fruit trees was common throughout England. In Sussex the wassailing took place on Christmas Eve. In Devonshire it was New Year's Eve when the farmer and his men went out to the orchard with a large jug of cider. There, encircling one of the best-bearing trees, they drank a toast and then fired their guns in conclusion. In some villages, it was customary for the young boys, known as "howlers," to rise early on New Year's morning, go to the orchards and, circling each tree, beat it with rods of willow while they chanted in chorus a song similar to this one. This custom was prevalent also in Germany and Belgium, in parts of France, and in the Tyrol. Dancing and singing around the trees, or beating upon them to make them bear, was common in all of these countries. Some Tyrolese farmers would go out on Christmas Eve, knock with bent fingers upon their trees, and bid them all wake up and bear fruit. A Slavonic custom consisted of threatening the trees with a hatchet if they did not produce fruit during the year.

Here we come a-wassailing

Brightly

Traditional English

1. Here we come a - was - sail - ing, A - mong the leaves so green. ___
   was - sail cup is made ___ of The rose - ma - ry tree, ___ And

Here we come a - wan - d'ring So fair ___ to be seen.
so ___ is your beer Of the best ___ bar - ley.

Love and joy come to you, And to you your was - sail

too, And God bless you and send you A Hap-py New Year, And God send you a Hap-py New Year. 2. Our

3. Bring us out a table,
   And spread it with a cloth;
   Bring us out a mouldy cheese
   And some of your Christmas loaf. *(Refrain)*

4. God bless the master of this house,
   Likewise the mistress too,
   And all the little children
   That round the table go. *(Refrain)*

❧ A Wassail Bowl ❧

"Simmer a small quantity of the following spices in a teacupful of water; namely, carda-mums, cloves, nutmeg, mace, ginger, cinnamon, and coriander. When done, put the spice to two, four, or six bottles of port, sherry, or Madeira, with one pound and a half of fine loaf sugar (pounded) to four bottles, and set all on the fire in a clean, bright saucepan; meanwhile, have yolks of 12 and the whites of 6 eggs well whisked up in it. Then, when the spiced and sugared wine is a little warm, take out one teacupful; and so on for 3 or 4 cups; after which, when it boils, add the whole of the remainder, pouring it in gradually, and stirring it briskly all the time, so as to froth it. The moment a fine froth is obtained, toss in 12 fine soft roasted apples, and send it up hot. Spices for each bottle of wine: 10 grains of mace, 46 grains of cloves, 37 grains of cardamums, 28 grains of cinnamon, 12 grains of nutmeg, 48 grains of ginger, 49 grains of coriander seeds."

(from an old English newspaper, the *Mark Lane Express*)

Good Evening

Bonsoir, Bonsoir

On New Year's Day in Rome, friends exchanged gifts (*strenae*) and presented them to the emperor. Such presents were a kind of charm, based on the belief that as the beginning was, so would the rest of the year be. In France, a Latinized country, January 1 is still the day when adults exchange gifts, the word for these being *étrennes* after the Latin *strenae*.

A free translation

Traditional French (Franche-Comte)

Brightly

1. Good eve - ning, oh good __ eve - ning, friend! The good New
1. Bon - soir, bon - soir, maî - tre de ces lieux! Voi - ci le

Year has come a - gain! Let eve - ry - one be hap - py here!
bon an qui est ve - nu, Que tout le monde est ré - jou - i!

Refrain

May you all have a good New Year! I wish you
Que Dieu vous mette en un bon an! Que Dieu vous

all a hap-py year!
donn' la bonne an-née!

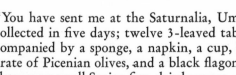

2. I pray you all most merry be,
   I pray you all most merry be,
   Let's dance and sing most merrily! *(Refrain)*

3. God bless this house and all within,
   Your friends and neighbors and your kin,
   Your friends and neighbors and your kin! *(Refrain)*

2. *Autant les grands que les petits,*
   Autant les grands que les petits,
   Que tout le monde est réjoui! (Refrain)

3. *Que Dieu bénisse cette maison,*
   Que Dieu bénisse cette maison,
   Toutes les latt' et les chevrons! (Refrain)

  The poet, Martial, complaining about the gifts he received at Saturnalia:

"You have sent me at the Saturnalia, Umber, all the presents you have collected in five days; twelve 3-leaved tablets, and seven toothpicks, accompanied by a sponge, a napkin, a cup, half a peck of beans, a wicker crate of Picenian olives, and a black flagon of Laletanian must: and with these some small Syrian figs, dried prunes, and a jar heavy with the weight of Libyan figs, I scarcely think the whole lot worth 30 sesterces, yet eight hulking Syrians carried it. How much more conveniently, and with no labour, might a boy have brought 5 pounds of silver plate!"

Now light one thousand Christmas lights

With spirit

Traditional Swedish

1. Now light one thou-sand Christ-mas lights On dark earth here to-night; One thou-sand, thou-sand al - so shine To make the dark sky bright.

2. Oh, once when skies were star-ry-bright, In sta - ble cold and bare, Sweet Ma - ry bore a son that night, A child both kind and fair.

Nu tändas tusen Juleljus

In the mythology of all men, darkness—black, empty and endless—has symbolized the Nothing out of which Life miraculously sprang. Life, the opposite of Death (dark nothingness), was Light. Light was therefore good, darkness was to be feared. Because this concept derived from perhaps the most basic of all human emotions, something of it still exists in the universal human subconscious.

From this basic concept has evolved man's use of lights in all his many and varied celebrations of joy, religious as well as secular. The most striking and obvious examples of this in modern times are Hanukkah, the Jewish "Feast of Lights," and Christmas. During Hanukkah, which is celebrated each year on the anniversary of the re-dedication of the Temple, a candle is lit on each of the eight nights in memory of the holy oil which miraculously burned for eight days when there was oil enough for only one day. During Christmas, candles are lit in most churches as a symbol of Christ, the Light of the world, and in many homes simply because they *are* Christmas.

Legends pertaining to miraculous or holy lights or fires come from every country and all cultures. A fairly typical one is a Hungarian song which tells of a miraculous stag with a thousand ends to his horns; on these horns burn a hundred thousand candles; "They burn without being lit; They go out of themselves."

All through Europe, and especially in Scandinavia where winter nights are longer and seemingly darker than elsewhere, Christmas without candles is unthinkable. St. Lucia's Day in Sweden is, in fact, a Swedish "feast of lights." On this day, December 13, the eldest daughter, called "Lussi" or *Lussibruden* ("Lucia bride"), gets up very early in the morning. Dressed in white and wearing a crown wreathed with whortleberry twigs and tall with lighted candles, she awakens the rest of the family, serving them coffee and cinnamon buns in bed. On that day, candles are kept lit in all the windows and in every room of the house.

3.

She named that dear baby Jesu,
Sweet Mary, meek and mild,
She cradled and she rocked him too,
That little tiny child.

4.

He came to bring us love and light,
To bring us peace on earth,
So let your candles shine tonight,
And sing with joy and mirth.

5.

Now light one thousand Christmas lights
On dark earth here tonight;
One thousand, thousand also shine
To make the dark sky bright.

Holly and Ivy

The lore connected with these plants is rich and the superstitions many, making holly and ivy, in one wording or another, a favorite phrase in traditional English folk song. In many carols, holly and ivy are symbolic of man and woman; some imply an age-old strife—who will wear the breeches, the master or the dame.

Traditional English

Not too quickly

1. The hol - ly and ___ the i - - vy, When they ___ are both ___ full grown, ___ Of all the trees that are in the wood, The hol - ly bears the crown. ___

2. The hol - ly bears ___ a blos - - som, As white as the li - - ly flower, ___ And Ma - ry bore sweet Je - sus Christ To be our sweet Sa - viour. ___

Chorus:

O the ris - ing of the sun, And the run - - ning 'of ___ the deer, ___ The play - ing of the merry or - gan, Sweet sing - ing in ___ the choir, ___ Sweet sing - ing in the choir. ___

3. The holly bears a berry,
   As red as any blood,
   And Mary bore sweet Jesus Christ
   To do poor sinners good. *(Chorus)*

4. The holly bears a prickle,
   As sharp as any thorn,
   And Mary bore sweet Jesus Christ
   On Christmas Day in the morn. *(Chorus)*

5. The holly bears a bark,
   As bitter as any gall,
   And Mary bore sweet Jesus Christ
   For to redeem us all. *(Chorus)*

The melody as given here was used by Mozart in a set of variations for violin and pianoforte. (See "Ariette" No. 25, published by Litolf)

MISCELLANEOUS CAROLS

Ever since the period of twelve days from the Nativity to Epiphany was declared a festal tide by the Church in 567, this time has been celebrated as the big holiday of the year in most countries where Christianity exists. In medieval England the twelve days were marked by an unbroken succession of gaieties. There were jousts, banqueting, caroling, and "mumming," which originally was a kind of pantomime dance performed by groups who were both costumed and masked. Minstrels and jugglers made music and mirth.

FOR THE TWELVE DAYS

In the Middle Ages, when few people could read, and entertainment as we know it did not exist, a minstrel was of necessity a many-talented fellow. One of these, in listing his accomplishments, after noting the many instruments he can play, says: "I can sing a song well and make tales and fables. I can tell a story against any man, I can make love verses to please young ladies, and can play the gallant for them if necessary. Then I can throw knives into the air and catch them without cutting my fingers. I can do dodges with a string most extraordinary and amusing. I can balance chairs and make tables dance. I can throw a somersault and walk on my head."

This English minstrel, of course, had his counterpart in Europe, where the twelve days were celebrated too, with feasting, pageantry, and song.

A Lord of Misrule in England, like the Abbot of Unreason in Scotland (both of whom were chosen by lot just as their predecessor was in ancient Rome during Saturnalia), ruled over all these festivities, many of which, too, were direct descendants of the Feast of Saturn.

In England some of the "pretty devices" preceding the banquets in the big halls on Twelfth Day are unbelievable-sounding confections which included castles with cannons and ships with guns which, at the proper moment, were fired against each other in semblance of a rousing battle. A description of another one of these devices from *The Cook and Confectioner's Dictionary* (1726) reveals the origin of the nursery rhyme "Sing a Song of Sixpence." It describes a pie out of which, when the lid is lifted, live birds fly, putting out the candles and causing a "surprising and diverting hurly-burly among the guests."

The songs included here are termed "miscellaneous" simply because, although they are Christmas songs, they could not be justifiably classified as belonging to any one specific type.

In this group particularly, it should be remembered that, generally speaking, carols did not have individual tunes, but were sung to popular melodies of the time. Tunes were used indiscriminately for both religious and secular works (an age-old custom that is documented as far back as the time of the ancient Hebrews); and very often a popular carol was sung to more than one tune.

A Mince Pie or a Pudding

Music and dance formed a major part of Shaker religious ritual, and songs were written for almost every kind of activity and for all festive occasions and holidays. Because it was considered a privilege to worship God with song and dance, no one who harbored evil or unkind thoughts was allowed to take part.

Shaker "welcome song"
New York State

Wel - come here, wel - come here, All be a - live and be of good cheer. Wel - come here, wel - come here, All be a - live and be of good cheer.

1. I've got a pie all baked com - plete, ___ Pud - ding, too, that's ver - y sweet.
2. Red ap - ples plen - ty, good nuts too, ___ Roast - ing in the fire for you.

(last time) C   Dmi.⁷   Emi.⁷

Wel - come here,   wel - come here,   All be a - live and be of good

Dmi.+⁴   C   Dmi.⁷   Emi.⁷

cheer. Wel - come here,   wel - come here,   All be a - live and be of good

Dmi.+⁴   C⁶

cheer. _____

3. Come, all good people, enter in
    The wind blows sharp, come in, come in.

4. You've got a flute, a little drum
    Make some music, don't be dumb.

5. Ding a-dong ding, a song to sing
    Let the merry music ring.

Verses 2-5 were written for this song as it appears here.

O COME, LITTLE CHILDREN

ihr kinderlein, kommet

Christoph von Schmid, 1768-1854

Johann A. P. Schulz, 1747-1800

1. O come, lit-tle chil-dren, O come, one and all! O come to the cra-dle in Beth-le-hem's stall; The

1. Ihr kin-der-lein, kom-met, o kom-met doch all! Zur Krip-pe her kom-met in Beth-le-hem's Stall, Und

bright star will guide us and show us the way To
seht, was in die - - ser hoch - hei - - li - gen Nacht Der

Je - sus who's ly - - ing a - sleep on the hay.
Va - - ter in Him - - mel für Freu - - de uns macht.

2. O look in the cradle
How sweet and how small
O see how the bright star
shines over the stall!
His mother has dressed Him,
the heavenly Child.
And angels proclaim Him,
so sweet and so mild!

2. *O Seht in der Krippe*
im nächtlichen Stall,
Seht hier bei des lichtleins
hellglänzendem Strahl,
In reinlichen Windeln
das himmlische Kind,
Viel schöner und holder
als Engel es sind.

3. The animals all seem
to know Mary's boy
And Joseph, with Mary,
beholds Him with joy;
The shepherds have entered
to Him love they bring,
While angels sing joyously,
merrily sing!

3. *Da liegt es, o Kinder*
auf Heu und auf Stroh,
Maria und Josef
betrachten es froh;
Die redlichen Hirten
knien betend davor
Hoch oben schwebt jubelnd
der Engelein Chor.

4. O come with the shepherds,
O come to the stall,
With hearts full of love
for the One who loves all!
O sing, little children,
to Him you adore;
Sing with the angels
sing peace evermore!

4. *O beugt, wie die Hirten*
anbetend die Knie
Erhebet die Händlein
und danket wie sie!
Stimmt freudig, ihr Kinder
wer sollt' sich nicht freu'n?
Stimmt freudig zum Jubel
der Engel mit ein.

To Bethle'm I Would Go

Czech

To Beth - le'm I would go,   To   see Him, say hel-lo;

I   have a crow-ing cock,_ black and trim,   A   pret- ty lit -tle cuck-oo, brown and slim;

These   I will give to Him.   Crow-ing cock   will   make Him gay,

Nev - er will fly a - way Lit - tle cuck - oo perch - ing near his ti - ny head,

Cal - ling sweet - ly to a - wake Him in His bed; These I will give to Him.

Cu - cuck - oo, Cu - cuck - oo, Hail to thee, Ho - ly Je - su!

Cu - cuck - oo, Cu - cuck - oo, Hail to thee, Ho - ly Je - su!

Christmas
is
Coming!

A jolly English round

Traditional English

1. Christ - mas is com - ing, The geese are get - ting fat!
2. If you have no pen - ny, A ha' pen - ny will do!

Please to put a pen - ny in the old man's ___ hat!
If you have no ha' pen - ny, a far - thing will do!

Please to put a pen - ny in the old man's hat!
If you have no far - thing, then God bless you!

Dame, get up and bake your pies

"As many mince pies as you taste at Christmas,
So many happy months will you have."

Traditional English

1. Dame, get up and bake your pies, Bake your pies, bake your pies;
2. Dame, what makes your maid-ens lie, Maid-ens lie, maid-ens lie;

Dame, get up and bake your pies,__ On Christ-mas Day in the morn-ing.
Dame, what makes your maid-ens lie,__ On Christ-mas Day in the morn-ing?

3. Dame, what makes your ducks to die,
   Ducks to die, ducks to die;
   Dame, what makes your ducks to die,
   On Christmas Day in the morning?

4. Their wings are cut and they cannot fly,
   Cannot fly, cannot fly;
   Their wings are cut and they cannot fly,
   On Christmas Day in the morning.

God Rest You Merry

Text appears here as it did when printed on a broadside about 1800.

Traditional English

1. God rest you mer - ry, gen - tle - men, Let noth - ing you dis - may, Re-
2. From God that is our Fath - er, The bles - sed an - gels came, Un-

mem - ber Christ our Sa - viour Was born on Christ - mas Day, To
to some cer - tain shep - herds, With ti - dings of the same; That

save poor souls from Sa - tan's power Which had long time gone a - stray,
there was born in Beth - le - hem The ___ Son of God by name.

And it's ti - dings of com - fort and joy, com- fort and joy; And it's ti - - dings of com - - fort and joy.

D.C.

3. Go, fear not, said God's Angels,
   Let nothing you affright,
   For there is born in Bethlehem,
   Of a pure Virgin bright,
   One able to advance you,
   And throw down Satan quite.
   (Chorus)

4. The Shepherds at those tidings,
   Rejoiced much in mind,
   And left their flocks a-feeding
   In tempest storms of wind,
   And strait they came to Bethlehem,
   The son of God to find.
   (Chorus)

5. Now when they came to Bethlehem,
   Where our sweet Saviour lay,
   They found him in a manger,
   Where Oxen feed on hay,
   The blessed Virgin kneeling down,
   Unto the Lord did pray.
   (Chorus)

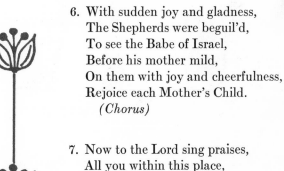

6. With sudden joy and gladness,
   The Shepherds were beguil'd,
   To see the Babe of Israel,
   Before his mother mild,
   On them with joy and cheerfulness,
   Rejoice each Mother's Child.
   (Chorus)

7. Now to the Lord sing praises,
   All you within this place,
   Like we true loving Brethren,
   Each other to embrace,
   For the merry time of Christmas,
   Is drawing on apace.
   (Chorus)

8. God bless the ruler of this House,
   And send him long to reign,
   And many a merry Christmas
   May live to see again.
   Among your friends and kindred,
   That live both far and near,
   And God send you a happy new Year.
   (Chorus)

MERRY CHRISTMAS
MERRY CHRISTMAS
MERRY CHRISTMAS
MERRY CHRISTMAS

Paraphrase by Tom Fletcher

Traditional Swedish

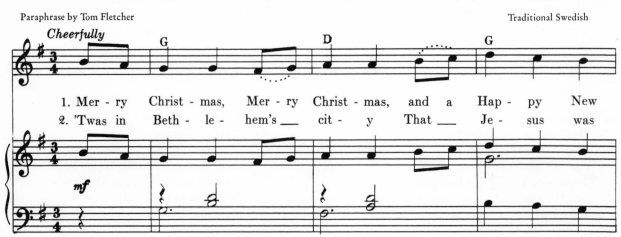

Cheerfully

1. Mer - ry   Christ - mas,   Mer - ry   Christ - mas,   and a   Hap - py   New
2. 'Twas in   Beth - le - hem's __ cit - y   That __   Je -   sus   was

Year!   Mer - ry Christ - mas,   Mer - ry Christ - mas,   And a   Hap - py   New
born.   'Twas in Beth - le - hem's __ cit - y   That __ Je - sus was

Year!   To __ fath - er and __ moth - er,   And   eve - ry - one   here!   To __
born.   A __ star   it was a - shin - ing,   Both   eve - ning and   morn.   A __

fath -   er and __   moth -   er   And   eve -   ry - one   here!
star   it was a -   shin -   ing,   Both   eve -   ning   and   morn.

D.C.

3. Oh I wish we could follow
   That star on this day,
   Oh I wish we could follow
   That star on this day.
   For all the way to heaven
   It lightens our way,
   For all the way to heaven
   It lightens our way.

OD BLESS THE MASTER OF THIS HOUSE

Paraphrase of traditional seventeenth century English carol

Tyrolean melody

1. God bless the mas-ter of this— house, And all that are there-
2. Then let us all most mer-ry— be, And dance with joy a-

in; It is the time of Christ-mas— now, With joy let us be-gin.
gain; Let's sing No-ël both loud and— clear; Sing out now, all good men.

Refrain

For the Sav-iour of all peo— — ple Was born this Christ-mas Day, To

bring   us   love   and   peace   on — earth;   For   Him   we   sing   and   play.

3. Let's get together, neighbors all,
   And fall no more at strife;
   Let every man with cheerfulness
   Embrace his loving wife. *(Refrain)*

4. Prepare some good and tasty food,
   Provide some warming cheer,
   And call your good friends all to come,
   That live both far and near. *(Refrain)*

"Scratche not thy head with thy fyngers
When thou arte at thy meate;
Nor spytte you over the table board;
See thou doest not this forget."

(From Salzman's *English Life in the Middle Ages*)

'Do not stuff too large mouthfuls in both cheeks. Do not keep your hand too long on the platter and put it in only when the other has withdrawn his hand from the dish."

(*The Fifty Courtesies of the Table*, published in Italy, 1480.)

Willie, Take Your Little Drum

Guillô, Pran Ton Tamborin

This carol first appeared in print in 1842, in *Noëls Bourgignons de Bernard de la Monnoye*. B. de la Monnoye lived 1641-1728.

1. Wil - lie, take your lit - tle drum; Rob- in, take your flute and come! When we hear the mu - sic gay, Tu - re - lu - re - lu, pat - a - pat - a - pan! When we hear the mu - sic gay, No - ël, No - ël, we say!

2. Long a - go was born a King, To __ Him we now do sing! Play your mu - sic sweet and clear, Tu - re - lu - re - lu, pat - a - pat - a - pan! Play your mu - sic sweet and clear, Sound-ing No - ëls __ of good cheer!

3. He was born on Christmas Day;
   Celebrate with us, come play!
   Let the music sound again,
   Turelurelu, patapatapan!
   Let the music sound again,
   Merry Christmas to all men!

COME, MAD BOYS, BE GLAD BOYS

This tune, under the title "Robin," appears in the *Fitzwilliam Virginal Book* and other sixteenth century collections. The words are seventeenth century.

Traditional English

1. Come, mad boys, be glad boys, for Christ-mas is here, And we shall be feast-ed with jol-ly good cheer; Then let us be mer-ry, 'tis St. Ste-phen's day, __ Let's eat and drink free-ly, there's noth-ing to pay.

2. My mas-ter bids wel-come, and so doth my dame, And 'tis yon-der smok-ing dish doth me in-flame; A-non, I'll be with you, though you me out-face, __ For now I do tell you I have time and place.

3. I'll troll the bowl to you, then let it go round,
   My heels are so light they can stand on no ground;
   My tongue it doth chatter, and goes pitter-patter,
   Here's good beer and strong beer, for I will not flatter.

4. And now for remembrance of blessed St. Stephen,
   Let's joy at morning, at noon, and at even;
   Then leave off your mincing and fall to mince-pies,
   I pray take my counsel, be ruled by the wise.

Ambered Chocolate

"Let any man who shall have drunk too deeply of the cup of pleasure, or given to work too many of the hours which should belong to sleep; who shall find the accustomed polish of his wit turned to dulness, feel damp oppression in the air and time hanging heavily, or be tortured by a fixed idea which robs him of all liberty of thought; let all such, we say, administer to themselves a good pint of Ambered Chocolate, allowing from 60 to 72 grains of amber to a pound, and they will see marvels. In my own particular way of specifying things, I call Ambered Chocolate the 'chocolate of the afflicted.'" (from Brillat-Savarin's *Physiologie du Goût*)

THE TWELVE DAYS

A rhyme or chant, also known in France. The lines are first found in *Mirth with-out Mischief,* a children's book published in London about 1780, where they are given as the words of a fireside memory-and-forfeits game. In the north of France, this game is called *Les dons de l'an*; in the west, *La foi de la loi.*

Uncertain origin

Traditional English

Brightly

1. On the first day of Christ-mas My true love sent to me A par-tridge in a pear

tree. 2. On the sec-ond day of Christ-mas My true love sent to me

Two tur-tle doves And a par-tridge in a pear tree. 3. On the

OF CHRISTMAS

La foi de la loi is sung *avec solemnité* and the sequence is: a good stuffing without bones, 2 breasts of veal, 3 joints of beef, 4 pigs' trotters, 5 legs of mutton, 6 partridges with cabbage, 7 spitted rabbits, 8 plates of salad, 9 dishes from the chapterhouse, 10 full casks, 11 beautiful full-breasted maidens, and 12 musketeers with their swords.　　(*Chants et chansons populaires des provinces de l'ouest*, J. Bujeaud, 1866.)

sixth day of Christ-mas my true love sent to me
sev-enth day
eighth day
ninth day
tenth day
e-lev-enth day
twelfth day

six geese a-lay-ing,
sev-en swans a-swim-ming, *(to 6)*
eight maids a-milk-ing, *(to 7)*
nine drum-mers drum-ming, *(to 8)*
ten pip-ers pip-ing, *(to 9)*
e-lev-en la-dies danc-ing, *(to 10)*
twelve lords a-leap-ing, *(to 11)*

Five gold __ rings, Four __ col-ly birds, Three French hens,

rit. *a tempo*

Two __ tur-tle doves And a par-tridge __ in a pear tree. (6-12.)On the tree.

(rit. last time)

six times D.S. last time only FINE

Index